241 F618

Date Due

NOV 29			
DEC 18			

No. 293   DEMCO-MADISON-WIS

The Historical

AIR MAIL

CATALOGUE

—o—

An Authoritive Catalogue

of

AIR MAIL STAMPS

and

HISTORICAL COVERS

1929

Price $2.00

Forwarding Charge Extra

Published by

K. LISSIUK PHILATELIC CO., Inc.

1476 Broadway, New York, N. Y., U. S. A.

Foreword

We present herewith a new and up to date catalogue of all Air Mail stamps.

This branch of stamp collecting has become so popular and so many collectors are interested in Air Mail stamps who care but little for General Issues that we find an authoritative catalogue indispensible.

This work has been compiled with great care and the pricing has also received the most painstaking consideration. We are confident that the Historical Air Mail Catalogue will meet with your approval.

Do not hesitate to write us on any subject connected with the Air Mail — we shall be glad to receive your letter.

We shall appreciate any reliable information you may have that is not mentioned in this book so we may incorporate it in our next edition. Numbers printed, variations of colors, and so forth are of special interest to us.

SCOPE OF THE CATALOGUE. — We have restricted our listings entirely to bona fide government issues and have excluded the various issues of private firms. Many of these companies do a great and useful work in transporting mail by air, notably in the Colombia Republic, Canada, Switzerland, etc. Nevertheless we feel that Air Mail stamps of established governments are diverse enough to fully occupy our attention. The future of Air Mail stamps is secure beyond question. As the status of private Air Mail issues is not so clearly established we prefer to ignore them.

FIRST FLIGHT COVERS — Covers of the early Pioneer Flights and the great Historical Flights that followed are eagerly sought after by collectors. The various other "First Flights" as of the Contract Air Mail and Air Port Dedications are so numerous as to discourage the average collector. We do not include them in this work.

K. Lissiuk Philatelic Co., Inc.

SPECIAL NOTICE

GUARANTEE	All stamps sold by us carry the unquestioned and unequivocal Lissiuk guarantee of genuineness.
PRICES	No discount is allowed on purchases of less than $1.00.
	All purchases over $1.00 and less than $10.00, 15% discount is allowed.
	All purchases over $10.00 and less than $50.00, 20% discount is allowed.
	All purchases over $50.00 a discount of 25% is allowed.
	The above scale of discounts applies to all individual purchases from this catalogue.
ACCUMULATIVE DISCOUNT	To those who prefer to have their purchases extend over a period of time we offer a liberal accumulative discount proposition. All you have to do is to present your receipted bills to us at the end of the year when an adjustment will be made with you based on the maximum discount you would be entitled to according to the above scale.
EXPERTIZING	Air Mail issues examined for genuineness at the fee of 50c. per stamp. Fees so received will be donated to the American Air Mail Society.
TERMS	Cash with order is the rule to all who are unknown to us. If you desire to open a charge or Approval account furnish us with your Society number or a suitable commercial reference, stamp dealer or bank preferred.
WANT LISTS	If you so desire we will keep on file any unfinished portion of your orders and will submit the missing stamps to you as they are obtained.

K. Lissiuk Philatelic Co., Inc.

The Conquest of the Air.

By NICHOLAS AFONSKY.

(Copyright by the McClure Newspaper Syndicate)

1. Humanity has always dreamed of flying. In the early stages of civilization the gift of flight was attributed to mythological characters and to the many gods. The Assyrian bulls were depicted with wings, and we all have heard of flying dragons and the flying horse, Pegasus. Phaeton, of Greek mythology, is shown above.

2. The story of Daedalus and his son Icarus, who were imprisoned by Minos, King of Crete, after they had constructed the famous Labyrinth, is the first in which ordinary human beings fly through the air through scientific preparation. Daedalus and his son gathered together all the loose bird feathers and then fastened them with wax into the shape of wings. With these they escaped from Crete. But Icarus, despite his father's warning flew too close to the sun and so melted the wax on his wings, falling into the sea. To this day, we have the Sea of Icarus, and Greece issued a set of occupation stamps in 1912 in Icaria with the head of Icarus as a center medalion.

3. An ancient Hindu manuscript tells of some strange "Aerial Chariot with sides of iron and clad with wings" which attacked the city of Dfwaska and hovering over it showered down deadly missiles upon the helpless inhabitants.

4. Archytas, the Pythagorean, is said to have made a dove of wood, a perfect automaton, which was endowed by some sort of mechanism that made it fly. It was balanced by various weights and "was put in motion by hidden and enclosed air." This dove automaton was spoken of by many Greek historians.

5. One of the strange myths of flying concerns Simon the Magician, founder of an anti-Christian sect in the first century in the time of Nero. To prove that there was nothing supernatural about the Ascension, the story goes, he made a fiery chariot, in which he flew several times over Rome.

6. Witches and sorcerers, according to popular tales, could always travel through the air. It is said that about 790 A. D., wishing to see if this really could happen, some prominent men living near Mount Pilatus, Switzerland, forced some of their poor neighbors to go up in a sort of balloon.

7.   The frightened wretches are said to have descended in the town of Lyons, where they were surroundered by a frenzied mob. The judges condemned them to be burned, but Bishop Agobard, after questioning them, decided that they had no evil intentions and allowed them to escape.

8.   In the year 1060 it is said that the monk, William of Malmesbury, England, made wings for himself, and then, in the presence of a great crowd of onlookers, jumped from a high tower. He fell, but he lived to tell how it feels to soar through the air like a bird, for his only injury was a broken leg.

9.   In the reign of one of the emperors Comnenus in the twelfth century, it is said that a Saracen tried to fly around the hippodrome at Constantinople. Mounting a tower, he spread out his arms, and the rods attached to them, and jumped. He crashed to the ground so badly injured that he soon died.

10.   Apparently the Far East had its early aspirations for flight. There is record of a balloon ascension at Canton, China, to celebrate the coronation of the Emperor Po-Kien in the beginning of the fourteenth century. This ascension is mentioned later by European visitors as an historical fact.

11.   In 1383, the Count of Burgundy wished to capture a citadel near Naples. A magician came to one of his generals and offered to take the citadel by forming a cloud on which his soldiers could cross over to the walls of the citadel in such numbers as to make victory certain.

12.   He was condemned by the Count to death, for he was looked upon as a man possessed of a devil. But he may have had an idea of some sort of balloon in which he hoped to carry soldiers enough to gain the citadel. Whatever his plan, it died with him.

13. Some believed that by hard training men could develop their relatively weak breast muscles, so that they could successfully use wings, and in the fourteenth and fifteenth centuries many children were made to practice with wings, in the hope that one of them would become a real birdman.

14. An Italian tried, in the seventeenth century, to fly from Scotland to France. When he fell at the foot of the battlements of Stirling Castle and broke his thigh, he stoutly maintained that if he had used eagle feathers instead of those of the barnyard fowl for his wings his flight would have been successful.

15. The Jesuit father, Francesco Lana, in 1670, suggested an airship held up by hollow globes of copper, diricted by oars and sails. The great error of this idea is the belief that a sail would be of any use in an airship. But still these early experimenters were working toward the invention of the dirigible.

16. A few years later the French locksmith, Besnier, made a flying machine of four collapsible planes held by rods over the shoulders. He did not try to rise with this machine, but many times in the next few years he and his pupils floated with it safely down from some eminence.

17. At the beginning of the eigteenth century a Russian peasant went one day to the Czar, Peter the Great. "I can fly," he said. "Fly if you can", answered Peter, "but remember that if you fall to the earth you will be beheaded." The peasant was not afraid of the Czar's stern words.

18. The peasant who wanted to be a birdman climbed to the top of a high tower, fastened on his clumsy wooden wings, and leaped. He fell to the foot of the tower and was killed. Peter came to him, knelt beside his body, prayed, and said: "You fell, but you were a brave man."

19. In 1709, Bartholomew de Guzman, a friar, went to the King of Portugal, saying he had a flying machine and asking protection for it. The king ordered death to ; nyone who copied it. But he was seized by the Inquisition as a heretic and put in jail, where it is supposed he died.

20. Emanuel Swedenborg, Swedish theologian, in 1714 mentioned his invention of a "Flying Vehicle, or the possibility of being sustained in the air, and being conveyed through it." Swedenborg's Flying Vehicle never got off paper, whereon he made very minute drawings and specifications for it.

21. Perhaps the first fairly successful flight was that of the Marquis de Bocqueville, who, in 1742, before a great multitude, flew part way across the Seine. The crowds were wildly enthusiastic as this birdman soared along, but when over the river he fell and was badly injured.

22. All the time men had an idea of flying machines held up by hollow globes. In 1755, Father Galien, a French monk, suggested that if men took big envelopes of canvas up to the tops of high mountains and filled them with rarified air, they could drag them down to use to lift great weights up again.

23. The first man to make experiments as the amount of wing surface necessary to keep a man in the air, calculated from birds, was Karl Meerwein, of Baden, who, in 1781, made a strange curved wing surface, to the middle of which he was fastened. He made one unsuccessful attempt to fly.

24. Men had long wished for some sort of gas lighter than air. In the year 1782 an Englishman, Cavallo, succeeded in filling soap bubbles with hydrogen, and the bubbles rose rapidly until they hit the ceiling. Experiments in the use of hydrogen led to the successful development of the balloon.

25. Stephen and Joseph Montgolfier, brothers, of Annonay, France, are credited with being the inventors in 1783 of the modern balloon. As they sat one night watching the smoke from the fire curl up the chimney one of them exclaimed, "Why couldn't smoke be made to lift bodies into the air?"

26. They began experimenting with smoke- filled paper bags, which they held over a brazier in which there was a fire. The bags so distended rose to the ceiling. The Montgolfiers probably knew that it was the hot air in the smoke, not the smoke itself, that made the bags light enough to rise.

27. The widow of a neighbor of the Montgolfiers, coming in one day when they were filling their paper bags, noticed their difficulty in holding them over the brazier. She suggested that they tie the bags down to the brazier, which they did, and thereafter their work of filling them was easy.

28. Encouraged by their experiments the brothers made bigger bags and filled them out of doors. Finally they made a big linen and paper bag which they filled with smoke. When it was filled to its 600 cubic feet capacity it broke the strings holding it down and soared away to a great distance.

29. On June 5, 1783, the crowd invited to the first exhibition of the Montogolfier brothers saw a big bag of paper and linen hanging limply from a rope. The bag was sewed fast to a big wooden ring, which was suspended over a deep pit in which was heaped wood for a fire.

30. At a signal, one of the brothers put a torch to the bonfire, and it burst into flame. Its smoke went through the hooped opening of the bag, and soon the big balloon began to fill. Two men tended the fire, adding fresh fuel, and eight men held down the big balloon with ropes until it was full.

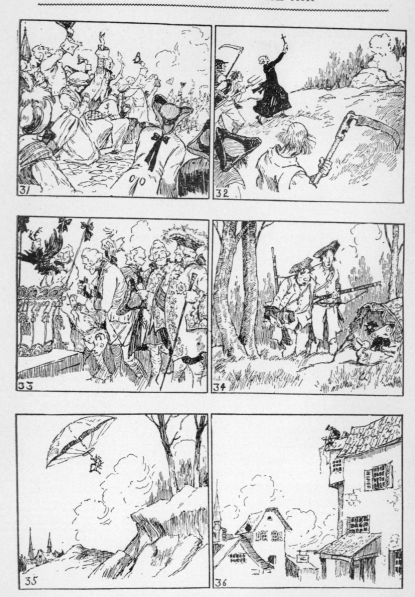

31. Then they let go the ropes and the huge globe ascended and sailed majestically away. Men shouted and threw their hats into the air, women wept and fell on their knees and prayed. A little later peasants in a field not far away were astonished to see a great moon descending upon them.

32. Armed with pitchforks and scythes, and led by the village priest, they attacked this supposed evil omen. They prodded and slashed at the gently heaving balloon, which had lighted on the ground, until it was all in shreds. Then they tied it to a horse's tail and beat him until he dashed away.

33. The news of the successful balloon ascension of the Montgolfier brothers spread quickly. The French king, Louis XVI, ordered a special demonstration at Versailles. This time a richly ornamented basket was hung from the balloon and to test its safety, a duck, a cock and a sheep were put in the basket.

34. The balloon, after the great fire had filled it with smoke, soared gently away. It came down a couple of miles away in woods. There two surprised gamekeepers hurried up to examine this strange visitor and found the passengers — duck, cock and sheep — quite unaffected by their voyage.

35. In the very year of the first authenticated balloon ascension a Frenchman named Le Normand experimented with a sort of parachute. He jumped from the branches of trees and landed safely on the ground, thus demonstrating perhaps for the first time the parachute idea.

36. Later Le Normand lost his nerve, and made further experiments by placing animals in baskets fastened below his parachute, and then dropping them from walls of buildings and tops of trees. As they always landed without injury his experiments roused great interest in the parachute theory.

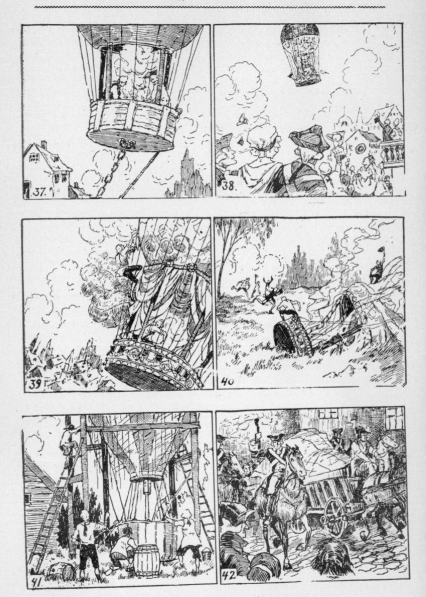

37. Pilatre de Rozier, in 1783, was the first man to make an authenticated ascent into the skies. Under his balloon swung a basket, in which a fire was kept burning to keep the balloon inflated. His first ascent was made with the balloon chained so that it could rise only ninety feet from the earth.

38. De Rozier returned to earth saying he had never before known such delightful sensation. A little later he and a friend made a free flight in a balloon. For twenty-five minutes they floated over Paris, to the astonishment of the crowds below, who feared the rarified air might injure them.

39. There was trouble in the balloon, but not from the rarified air. At first the two men, carefully keeping the fire burning, floated along delightfully. Suddenly they heard a crackling noise and saw tiny tongues of flame breaking out on the balloon above them, which had become overheated.

40. They had come prepared for this contigency. While de Rozier put out the fire in the grate, so that the balloon would descend, his friend repeatedly wet a big sponge in a bucket of water and extinguished the little flames. Slowly the balloon sank, and the two men came safely to earth.

41. Montgolfier and de Rozier knew nothing of the recent experiments with hydrogen, but inflated their balloons with heated air. The French brothers Robert and a M. Charles decided to make a hydrogen balloon. They experimented with the envelope, finally making it of fine silk, varnishing it with a solution of gum elastic.

42. At last they had it finished. Through a stop-cock in the neck of the bag they inflated it. They raised money for it through a popular subscription and were to give an exhibition on August 27, 1783. Long before daylight it was tied to a cart, and dragged to the Champs de Mars outside Paris.

43. At five in the afternoon a booming cannon gave word to the waiting crowd that the balloon was about to rise. As it was released from the chains that held it, it shot up into the sky over three thousand feet, and finally disappeared behind heavy rain clouds which had come up.

44. Far above the rain the balloon floated safely along, and finally after floatnig fifteen miles it landed safely in an open field. The three men who were responsible for it had successfully conducted the first ascension cf a hydrogen-filled balloon and opened a big future for this type of air travel.

45. "What is the use of a balloon, anyway?" somebody asked Benjamin Franklin at the time of the Montgolfier exhibitions in Paris. "What is the use of a baby?" countered Franklin, smiling. Americans showed interest in the development of ballooning, and in 1783 there was an ascension at Philadelphia.

46. M. Blanchard and a Benedictine monk, in 1784, took up a balloon fitted with wings and a rudder. An accident brought the balloon bumping to earth, and the monk, frightened got out. But Blanchard went up again, and was almost overcome with cold at the great height to which he soared.

47. A little later Blanchard succeeded in making the greatest balloon trip up to that time when he crossed the English Channel with Dr. Jeffries, an American physician, in January, 1785. Halfway across they began to descend, and threw out sandbags, bottles, their compass, rope and boxes.

48. In spite of their efforts to lighten the balloon they continued to fall. Finally they began to throw overboard some of their clothing. Just then they caught sight of the distant French coast. Suddenly the balloon stopped falling, and a little later they floated safely over land and descended near Caiais.

49. After the first successful flight across the channel, by the Frenchman, Blanchard, his countryman de Rozier tried the same trip in a double balloon, a hydrogen balloon above, a fire balloon below, but partway across the channel both balloons burst into flame and de Rozier fell and was killed.

50. In the same year, 1785, a young Italian, the Chevalier Vincent Lunardi, made the first balloon ascension in England. His balloon, of striped red and blue, was filled with hydrogen. After his successful flight he was lionized by the British people, and feted and entertained by the rich.

51. Meusnier, called the father of the modern dirigible, suggested air bags or balloonets inside the balloon proper. These, pumped full of air. would help keep the balloon inflated when the gas began to escape. He advocated a boat-shaped car, and propellers worked by hand pulleys.

52. The Duke de Chartres in a balloon of this sort, fitted with oars and rudder, made an ascent in 1784. The opening through which gas should escape became closed by an air bag inside. The balloon began to swell, but the duke, with his sword, gashed the envelope and prevented a tragic explosion.

53. Blanchard, famous Frenchman who first crossed the English Channel in a balloon, became interested in parachutes, In 1793, in a public ascension over Strasvourg, he dropped from his balloon a dog, with a little parachute attached to his back. The crowd below were wild with delight when it landed.

54. A little later this brave man made the first human parachute descent. Jumping from a balloon, he fell gradually until he was near the ground. Then his parachute gave way and he crashed to the earth with a broken leg. But he was still firm in his belief in the parachute as a "life belt."

55. M. Andre Garnerin, another Frenchman, a little later made a descent from a balloon at a great height without injury. He, like his predecessors, had a parachute umbrella that opened as the air rushed up under it. Garnerin later gave a demonstration in England and was badly injured by a fall.

56. But ten years later the parachute for the first time proved a life saver when a balloonist named Kuparanto, making an ascension over Warsaw, threw himself from his balloon which caught fire in mid-air, and, by means of his parachute, fell safely to the earth far below him.

57. In its early days the balloon was used on the battlefield. In 1794, when the French and the Austrians were at war, the French Captain Coutelle, under fire from the Austrians, who tried to prevent him from going up, rose to a height of 1,000 feet, where he was safe from the Austrian guns.

58. There Coutelle sat, safe from gun fire, watching the outraged Austrians and dropping notes to the French forces below him to tell them the movements of the enemy. The French won a victory, though the Austrians, having no observation balloons, called this new kind of warfare unfair.

59. The French began to dream of great military uses for the balloon. In 1800 General Resnier thought of the practicability of sending a French army corps to England by balloons travelling over the channel. Engravings of the time show the ideas the French had for reaching England in this way.

60. Resnier built a flying machine with flapping wings and jumped off the ramparts of Angouleme. He fell into the river the first time but, nothing daunted, tried again and again. Once, jumping from a height of 200 feet; he traveled 600 feet before gliding to the earth.

61. Sir George Gayley, the "father of British Aeronautics," did much in England in the early part of the 19th century to further aviation. He familiarized himself with steam engines, and concluded that none would give power enough with sufficient lightness to be serviceable in flying machine.

62. Gayley was specially interested in gliding flight instead of flaping-wing flight. He gave much attention to actual bird wings, studying their construction and action. He made a gliding apparatus with a surface of about 200 square feet which went safely from the top of a hill to the valley below.

63. A top which Gayley made, worked by a bow and a tight cord, and based on a clumsy toy called a Chinese top, attracted great attention. It is now known as a helicoptor toy or flying top. In this and other devices Gayley worked out many theories that led later to successful aviation.

64. It has been said that Gayley made a flying machine with an engine driven by successive explosions of gunpowder discharged by a detonator. He induced his coachman to take a ride in it. The coachman, frightened, jumped as it was leaving the ground and broke his leg and the machine.

65. Men were beginning to work toward the idea of a practical flying machine. Several men devised unsuccessful flying machines, one of which was kept aloft by a balloon attached to it. In 1811, Thomas Walker of Hull, England, designed a flying machine with a sail. But it wouldn't fly.

66. Other men were working along the lines of the dirigible. One of these was Leppig, who constructed a long balloon, from which hung a fin propeller, worked by hand by means of complicated ropes. This was not a practical apparatus, but it was another step toward the eventual perfection of it.

67. It was a little later than this that Charles Green, in 1836, on a fine autumn day, started on a long journey. His balloon, the famous "Great Nassau," was provisioned for several days. Green was going as long as he could stay up. He floated across the channel, and darkness overtook him.

68. All through the night Green and his companion floated in the darkness, anxiously trying to see from the big basket hung under the balloon where they were. When dawn broke, they saw that they were safe over the land, and in the course of the morning brought their balloon down in Germany.

69. In 1837 an Englishman, Cocking, designed a parachute like an umbrella blown inside out. The upper rim was of tin, the sides of cloth, and from it hung a basket for him. He persuaded the famous balloonist Green to fasten the parachute beneath his balloon, the Nassau, and make an ascension.

70. Green had refused to make the ascent with Cocking, but finally gave in to his pleadings. Green persisted in refusing to free the parachute, but Cocking overcame this difficulty by arranging a contrivance by which he could free himself. At 5,000 feet up Cocking called goodby and let go.

71. Freed by the considerable weight of the parachute and Cocking, Green's balloon bounded high into the air, tossing from side to side. It was only with the greatest difficulty that Green and his companion got the big balloon into control again. They landed safely, not knowing Cocking's fate.

72. Once free of the balloon, Cocking's parachute plunged rapidly to earth, swinging backward and forward. Not far above ground, weakened by the strain of its sudden fall, it went to pieces and the brave man who had staked his life on its safety crashed to earth. He died a few moments later.

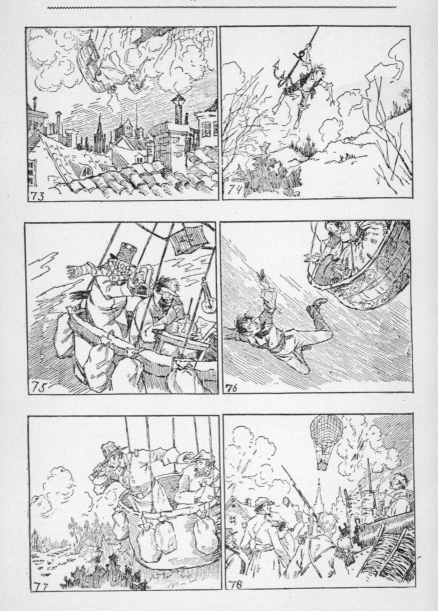

73. While the science of ballooning was progressing steadily, many exciting incidents occured in connection with it. One was the tragic death of Mme. Blanchard, whose husband was killed in a balloon acc'dent. She ascended to give an aerial display of fireworks in Paris, but her balloon became ignited, and she fell to death on the housetops.

74. One of the spectators of a balloon ascension in France, a little boy named Guerin, was caught by the trailing anchor of the balloon. He hung on the rope of the anchor for his life, and for about fifteen minutes sailed through the air, finally landing safely when the hot-air balloon cooled off and came dawn.

75. Before it became much more than a source of amusement, the balloon was used to investigate conditions in the upper air. An ascension for this purpose was made over a hundred years ago by two French philosophers, Gay Lussac and Buit, who studied magnetism and electricity at different heights from the earth.

76. In 1824 an aeronaut named Harris took his fiancee up in balloon at London. The balloon began to fall. He threw overboard all his ballast, but the balloon still fell. Then he jumped overboard and was killed. The lightened balloon came safely to earth with his fiancee.

77. In the American civil war balloons were first used for military purposes in this country. The Northern army used observation balloons to keep watch of Confederate movements around Richmond, Virginia, and the observers gained knowledge that was of great value to the military authorities.

78. By 1870, when the Franco-Prussian war was fought, balloons had been so developed that they became of greater military use. During the siege of Paris by the Germans in 1870-71, sixty-six balloons left the city at different times carrying messages and passengers.

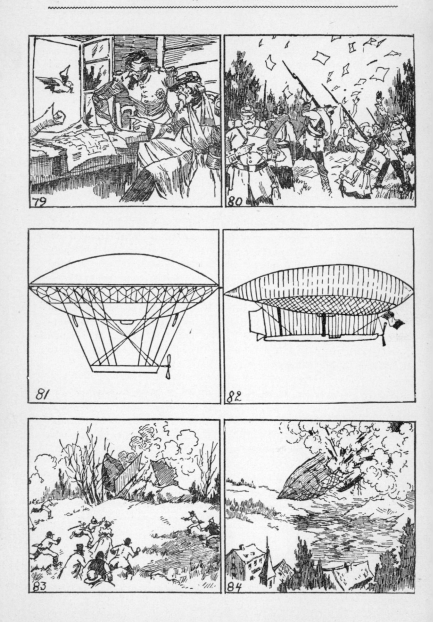

79. Another use for these balloons was to take carrier pigeons from the beleaguered city, whole flocks of them, and by means of them send messages back to Paris from the outside. Warfare was beginning to assume a somewhat more modern aspect with its use of free and captive balloons.

80. One French balloonist dropped thousands of warning messages down over the German lines. These messages warned the Germans that, in spite of the siege of Paris, France would continue the fight to the bitter end. This service paralleled the world-war dissemination of propaganda by airplane.

81. While the Franco-Prussian war was still in progress, the first military dirigible was built by Dupuy de Lome for the French government. It was successfully tried out in 1872. Though a light steam engine had been used in other balloons, its propellor was driven by hand by a crew of eight men.

82. Men were retarded from developing the dirigible by the lack of a light powerful engine. Renard and Krebs developed their dirigible, driven by an electric motor. They christened the balloon, "La France" and gave an exhibition near Chalais on August 9, 1884. They made fourteen miles an hour in a successful trip.

83. Germany watched the progress France was making in the development of balloons, and in 1880 Baumgarten and Wolfert, two Germans, ascended in a cigar-shaped dirigible, with wings or sails at the sides, and three oars suspended below it. One of the passengers overbalanced the ship, and it crashed to earth.

84. They used a benzine motor. A few years later, after Baumgarten's death, Wolfert built a new dirigible. He made several successful ascensions, but finally his benzine vaporizer caused an explosion, from which the ship caught fire in mid-air. He and his assistant were killed, as the ship crashed flaming to the ground.

85. The researches of John Stringfellow in England led to progress, though the aeroplane he made, which flew perfectly in a big hall, never flew outdoors. About the same time, 1854, LeBris, a French sailor, inspired by the steady flight of the albatross, which kept pace with the swiftest ships, decided to experiment with flying.

86. After studying a dead albatross, LeBris, as he said, "Comprehended the whole mystery of flight." He built an artificial bird, which could float on water. To gain impetus for flight he fastened the bird to the rail of a horse-drawn cart by a rope which he could loosen quickly. Men walking by the cart held the bird in place.

87. At a signal from LeBris they let go the bird. It rose to a height of 300 feet. The driver of the cart had become entangled in the rope which had tied the bird to the cart. He served to balance it beautifully, like a sort of dragging anchor, but his frightened screams forced LeBris to descend.

88. In his descent he only broke one wing of his plane. After he had it mended, he rose again, but his machine descended in a quarry and was smashed, along with the daring aeronaut's leg. He later made another machine that would fly, but it, too, came to grief. Then LeBris gave up flying, and later served in the Franco-Prussian war.

89. The man who is sometimes credited with giving the airplane its first real start was the German, Otto Lilienthal, who from boyhood had been trying to devise some sort of wings which would carry the human body into the air. He experimented with kites with curved wings and found to his delight that they rose rapidly.

90. He was a poor engineer, but he worked hard and saved money. Finally, with his savings, he built a pair of wings, arched like those of birds which he had studied. This was a fairly satisfactory glider, and with it attached to his body he soared from hillsides down into the valley. But he could not fly like a bird.

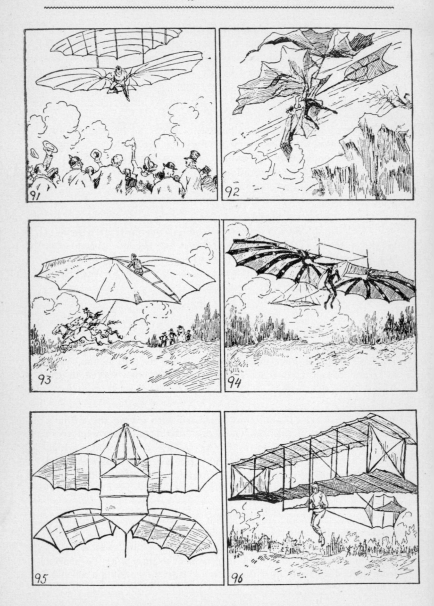

91. Each gust of wind tipped Lilienthal, now this way and now that. But by skillful balancing of his body he managed to keep himself from tipping over. He used to practice for hours together, to the delight of crowds of spectators, who called him the bird man, and wondered at his ability to soar over their heads.

92. Finally, becoming reckless, he flew one day in 1896 in strong wind with his big double glider wings. The wind caught him high above the earth and, though he struggled to regain control of his unwieldy apparatus, he crashed to the ground where, a few moments later, horrified onlookers found him dead.

93. Next came Percy S. Pilcher, a young English marine engineer, who built a glider called the Gull. Treating it like a kite, he fastened it on and had it hauled out into a field attached by a rope to strong horses. When it had been caught by the wind he unfastened the rope and went soaring through the air.

94. Pilcher had followed Lilienthal's work with great interest. He improved on the Gull in a second glider called the Hawk. One October day in 1899 when he was making a flight in this glider near Oxford, an imperfect part of the apparatus broke and the daring and ambitious young flyer crashed to earth.

95. The next man to help pave the way for the great accomplishment of the Wright brothers in the making of a practical flying machine was Chanute. In 1896 he built several large machines, one of them a Lilienthal glider. On this he made several successful glides in the United States in the next few years.

96. But he decided that the principle of this machines was wrong and devised a big double-deck glider in which he made over seven hundred safe glides. The big machine was in reality the prototype of the first Wright airplanes which brought lasting fame to them and opened up the era of modern flying.

97. Andree's trip in search of the North Pole was one of the most dramatic of all journeys by air. Salomon Auguste Andree was born in Sweden in 1854. He studied engineering, and then entered the government employ. In 1892 he was given leave to undertake scientific aerial navigation.

98. In the summer of 1893 he made his first balloon ascension, and later that year was carried out to sea in the balloon. He tried to reach the coast of Finland, but his balloon lost its buoyancy, and, though he threw out all balast, he finally fell into the sea near a small island.

99. He scrambled ashore, and lay there all night, with a sprained leg, unable to attract attention. In the morning, cold and suffering from his hurts, he managed to wave his clothes about until a boatman saw him and came to his rescue. He was none the worse for his exciting experience.

100. Andree, tremendously impressed with the possibilities of long balloon flights, finally went with his pet scheme to the Academy of Science of Sweden. That was a flight to the North Pole by balloon. The Academy sponsored the plan, and money was raised by national subscriptions.

101. Andree's balloon was finally made in Paris. Andree paid much attention to his supplies of arms and ammunition, preserved foods packed in labeled packets of strong fabric, enough to last for four months being carried, snow shoes, sledges and the framework of a boat that could be easily assembled.

102. In 1896 he went to Dane's island to make the dash to the pole. But that summer the winds were adverse, and the flight was postponed a year. On July 11, 1897, Andree with three companions, started from Dane's island to blow with the winds over the pole to Siberia or Alaska.

103. On July 22, one of Andree's homing pigeons, carrying an "all goes well" message, was killed by some fisherman near Spitzbergen. On August 31, and in May of the next year, buoys bearing messages dated July 11, reporting safe progress, were picked up. That was the last ever heard of Andree.

104. Years later, a missionary reported an Eskimo tribe from the far north, who had told of the coming of a "'white house" out of the sky, with two starving white men, who shortly died. They showed the missionary ropes like those on Andree's balloon which, they said, hung from the "house."

105. At about the same time Santos-Dumont and Zeppelin came into the history of dirigibles. Zeppelin fascinated in ballooning in the American Civil War when, as a member of a volunteer German corps in the Union army, he went up several times in captive observation balloons.

106. In the Franco-Prussian war the young Zeppelin again proved his love for ballooning when he went, as a member of an observation flight, far into French territory. He was only one of the four observers to return alive to the German lines from this daring trip into enemy territory.

107. Zeppelin now went to work to perfect some sort of dirigible balloon. He appealed for money to a rich American newspaper owner who answered that he had no money to waste on "crazy inventors." He appealed to the Kaiser, who referred him to a committee. They called it impracticable.

108. Nothing daunted, Zeppelin persevered until he had money enough to begin work on his great airship. The King of Wurtemberg helped him, and in July, 1900, it was ready for a trial flight. It was a dirigible, the longest ever built, with two cars, and engines of about thirty horsepower.

109. Five years after his first successful dirigible, Zeppelin had a second one ready, with lighter engines. But it had too great lifting power, and could not be operated at a safe level. It was destroyed during the night after its first flight by a gale on Lake Constance, where it was anchored.

110. The Zeppelin III became the kernel of the great German air war fleet. It carried eleven passengers for sixty-nine miles, and performed other feats that at the time were considered remarkable. The Zeppelin IV, after a world-record trip of twenty-one hours, was destroyed, after landing, by fire.

111. Zeppelin, now an old man, though beset by misfortunes, had the full backing of his countrymen and government. The Kaiser honored him as the conqueror of the air, and knighted him. In June, 1909, he made a voyage of over 900 miles, but his airship collided with a tree and was badly damaged.

112. In April 1911, the first aerial passenger Zeppelin ship, carrying the first aerial restaurant, started out with thirteen passengers. They ran into a gale of wind and rain, and finally plunged earthward to land in the treetops with great injury to the ship, but little to its passengers.

113. At the same time that Zeppelin was making his big dirigibles in Germany, a Brazilian, Alberto Santos-Dumont, was working on navigable balloons in France. He made his first ascent, with a non-rigid dirigible, in September, 1898. But when just off the ground his balloon was blown into the trees.

114. His second attempt to rise, a few days later, was successful. He flew satisfactorily for some time, but when descending realized that he was falling too rapidly. He called for some boys flying a kite to grasp his guide rope and run with it against the wind, and this brought him down safely.

115. In 1901 Santos-Dumont successfully steered one of his dirigible around the Eiffel Tower at Paris, but on his return his motor stopped in mid-air and his airship was blown into some chesnut trees. There spectators found him unhurt, standing in the basket of the airship up in the trees.

116. Another trip of this daring man nearly came to grief. His balloon lost gas over Paris and began to sag. He stopped the motor and descended finally to catch on the roof of a hotel. There firemen rescued him by ropes let down from above from his precarious perch in his wicker basket.

117. Santos-Dumont liked to do surprising things with his small airships. One day he flew to his own doorstep in Paris and parked his airship in the street in the front of it while he went into the house to have breakfast. It was an enthusiastic crowd that greeted him when he came out.

118. Once, when flying over Monte Carlo, he was blown over the Mediterranean. The sun's heat caused the gas in his partly inflated balloon to expand and he was carried toward the houses of Monte Carlo and dropped into the sea.

119. In 1908 he showed his dragon-fly or demoiselle, a small, almost toy-like monoplane that weighed only 242 pounds. It was so light that a puff of wind would upset it while it was running along the ground. However, its famous designer was never seriously hurt.

120. On one occasion Santos-Dumont's dirigible caught fire, but he patted the flames out with his panama hat. He placed his last three dirigibles at the disposal of the French government. Though none of them was suitable for military purposes, his work did much to stimulate French military flying.

121. The Wright Brothers, of Dayton, Ohio, who owned a bicycle shop there, are called the inventors of the modern aeroplane. From boyhood they were interested in flying, and read everything about it. They were especially interested in Lillenthal's glider, and determined to make one of their own.

122. For two years they studied everything about flying, and then made a glider on the order of Chanute's biplane. To work this glider, the operator lay face downward on the center of the lower plane. It was necessary, of course, to start from a height to get impetus to make the glider work.

123. For several years the Wrights practiced quietly at Kill Devil Dunes, on the coast of North Carolina, where the winds were favorable. They developed an elevating plane on their wings to make their glider go up and down, a wing-warping device for stability, and a rudder to turn it.

124. They realized that to go farther they must have a motor. In 1903 they flew the first real aeroplane with a four-cylinder gasoline engine. Their first flight lasted twelve seconds. They offered their ideas to France, but France failed to realize their importance.

125. Santos-Dumont meanwhile developed a biplane glider with an eight cylinder motor, in which he rose from the water in 1906 and flew 200 feet. This was first officially recorded European airplane flight. In 1908 the Wrights-Orville in America, Wilbur in France — began a series of flights.

126. Henry Farman, an Englishman living in France, made one of the early records. He had a big reputation as an automobile racer when he turned his attention to flying. In 1908, in a 1400 Voisin machine, he made the first recorded flight of an airplane carrying a passenger.

127. Glenn Curtiss, who was in many bicycle races and made the first motorcycles, became associated with Alexander Graham Bell and other scientists in aerial experiment. In 1908 in the June Bug he made the first previously announced flight and won the Scientific American trophy.

128. On September 12, 1908, the first recorded airplane fatality occurred, when Orville Wright, flying at Fort Myer, near Washington, D. C., had some sort of accident that sent his plane crashing to the ground. Wright was badly hurt, but, his passenger, Lieutenant Selfridge, was killed.

129. The London Daily Mail offered a thousand-pound prize for the first flight of the English Channel. In July, 1909, Hubert Latham and Bleriot, both French, were waiting at Calais for weather favorable for the crossing. For days contrary winds held them back.

130. Finally, on Jully, 24, the weather seemed favorable, and the two men started. Lotham was ahead, when his plane stopped and he glided down into the Channel. He swung his feet up to a crossbar to keep them from getting wet, lighted a cigarette, and waited for a French destroyer.

131. In the meantime Bleriot made a good flight. Fifty minutes after leaving France he saw Deal. He landed near Dover Castle, where only one man, a French journalist, saw his descent. But he was soon acclaimed by the world as the first man to cross the Channel by airplane.

132. Next day Latham started again from Calais. In twenty minutes he was almost at Dover. There the crowds watching from the English coast saw his plane lurch forward and fall into the water. He was quickly rescued, with only a cut from his motor goggles as a result.

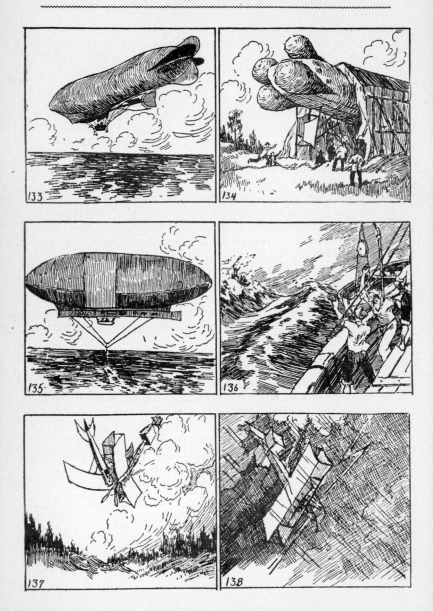

133. Airship flight was progressing all this time. In 1907 the Patrie, a dirigible, had drifted from her moorings in France and without pilot or passenger, had crossed the Channel and come down in Ireland. Before she could be secured, however, she drifted out over the Atlantic and was lost.

134. On October 26, 1910, the Lebaudy, brought from France by England, crossed the Channel safely with a crew of eight men. A little later another dirigible crossed the Channel successfully from France, but her top was ripped off when she was being pulled into the too-small shed provided for her.

135. In 1910 occurred the interesting failure of Walter Wellman with a crew of four to cross the Atlantic. He had previously tried — but failed — to fly to the North Pole. His ship, the America, carried a new sort of guide rope, an equilibrator, which from the start tended to pull it down.

136. Finally the America sent out a wireless distress signal, and a nearby steamer, the Trent, went to her aid. After maneuvering for several hours the crew of the America — and their black cat — let loose their lifeboat from the airship, and were picked up from the sea by the crew of the Trent.

137. People had long been predicting a mid-air collision. The first serious accident of this sort was at Milan, Italy, in October, 1910, when a tiny monoplane, descending, struck a larger biplane and the two planes fell to earth locked together. Neither pilot was killed, but one was badly hurt.

138. Another early accident that attracted much attention at the time occurred when a pilot named Ehrmann was caught in a thunder storm. Before he could bring his plane to earth it was struck by lightning, and burst into flames. Strangely enough the pilot landed unhurt.

139. Several attacks by eagles are on record — one when they attacked two contestants in Paris to Madrid flight in 1911, in the Pyrenees. Gilbert, one of these pilots, frightened his assailant by firing a revolver, The other pilot, Vedrines, got away from his eagle by a quick descent.

140. Vedrines won the race — a distance of 727 miles. Just after he had left Paris, there was a terrible accident at the starting field when one of the contestants lost control of his monoplane, which plunged into the crowd, injuring many people and killing Bertaux, the minister of war.

141. In 1910 occurred the great London to Manchester flight for a prize of 10,000 pounds, offered by the London Daily Mail. An Englishman, Claude Graham-White, and a Frenchman, Louis Paulhan, were ready on April 28. The weather was bad, so Graham-White went to sleep in his hotel.

142. Paulhan, however, decided to risk bad weather, and started off. As soon as news of his start reached Graham-White's advisers, they hurried to waken him. He did not not even wait to don heavy enough clothing, but started out in the dusk, and before dark flew over a hundred miles to Lichfield.

143. Knowing he must make up for lost time, Graham-White did an unprecedented thing. He decided to go on in the dark. Lamps were placed at the ends of the field and he rose. Three-quarters of an hour later he was seen in the moonlight over Rugby, but at dawn he was forced down.

144. In the meantime Paulhan, after a good night's rest, started early in the morning to finish his flight. He followed the railroad tracks, and landed victor at the field chosen for the finishing point amidst a tremendous ovation from a crowd, many of whose members had never seen an airplane.

145. In 1909, at Rheims, France, occurred the first aviation meeting ever held, which did much to convince the world that flying was really practicable. As many as five airplanes were in the air at the same time at the meeting, and seven flights of more than hour made another very impressive record in the public mind.

146. Leon Delagrange was one of the important fliers of that time. Studying art at the Beau Arts he met, as fellow students, Henry Farman and Gabriel Voisin, who later became noted fliers. He was killed at Boideaux in 1910 when the left wing of his monoplane crumpled.

147. In October, 1910, Captain Matsievitch, a Russian flier and Nihilist, is said to have been ordered to take a high military officer up in his plane and have an accident fatal to both passenger and pilot. Matsievitch had a chance to take up the dignitary, but just as he was about to start detectives came up to him.

148. They made him take an oath to protect his passenger's life. Matseivitch considered the oath as sacred and brought his passenger safely to earth again. Then the Nihilists ordered Matsievitch to kill himself within 24 hours. Next day he let his airplane, high in the air, plunge to earth. He was picked up dead in the wreckage.

149. The first flight across the United States was made by C. P. Rogers in 1911, when he tried for a $50,000 prize. He left New York September 17, reached Pasadena November 5, — and lost the prize, which allowed only 30 days. He made 68 stops, and helped pay his expenses selling a beverage in the towns where he stopped.

150. Though the transcontinental flight has since been made without stop in about 24 hours, Rogers record was remarkable. He had many slight accidents en route. Another 1911 record was made when E. B. Ely flew from the shore near San Francisco to the deck of the battleship Pennsylvania and back again.

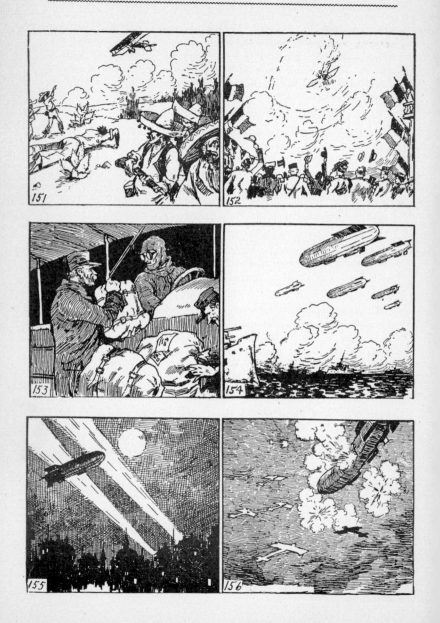

151. It was about this time that the airplane was first used for military purposes, when the United States — February, 1911 — sent Charles Hamilton flying over the Mexican border near Juarez to observe fighting there in a revolution. About the same time France used airplanes in military maneuvers in the Mediterranean.

152. The French airplanes — which then flew at an altitude of 1,500 feet, with a maximum of forty miles an hour, records which would seem insignificant today — were pronounced by the French war minister "marvelous instruments of war." A little later Pegoud, a French flier, for the first time looped the loop in an airplane in France.

153. Altitude, speed and duration records were much increased in the years just before the war, and several countries, including the United States, established flying corps or aviation schools in connection with their armies and navies. Mail was carried for the first time by airplane between Ghent and Brussels in 1913.

154. With the breaking out of the World War in 1914, scientists in the different countries involved worked with concentration on improving airplanes and dirigibles. In Germany the great Zeppelins, that did so much damage and brought so great terror to the Allied noncombatants, were wonderfully developed.

155. The German Zeppelins soon began to make night air raids over England, especially when there was a moon. English cities built up a special raid defense. Streets and houses were darkened, sirens were installed to warn the populace of the coming of raiders, and scout planes were kept in readiness to ascend and chase off the raiders.

156. One of the famous raids occurred on September 2, 1916, when the big German dirigibles flew over the eastern counties of England, and over London. The scout planes jumped into action, pursued the raiders, and succeeded in pumping one so full of shot that it burst into flames and fell to the ground.

157. At the beginning of the war airplanes were used for obser-vation, photographic, bombing and scout work. Before long they were fitted with rapid fire guns and became effective fighting machines. Richthofen, a German, with eighty Allied planes to his credit, was perhaps the greatest of all aces.

158. He organized a Flying Circus of German fliers. All the planes were painted in bright colors, his own flaming red. He used to drop notes over Allied airdromes, telling the fate of Allied aces he had shot down. So when he was killed the Royal Flying Corps dropped a note on the German aidrome, giving the news.

159. Colonel William Bishop, with 72 victories to his credit, ranks as the British ace. His engine went dead after he had brought down his first plane. He decided to glide as near his own lines as possible and landed in a deserted German village which he found to his great joy the British had just taken.

160. Captain Albert Ball was another great British pilot, with at least 44 planes to his credit. He used to get under his enemy and fire up into the engine or gasoline tank, and so send his opponent's plane crashing in flames to earth. He was killed in a spectacular fight with Richthofen's Circus well behind the German lines.

161. Captain Rene Fonck was the premier French ace, with 75, victories credited to him, more than any other Allied pilot. He worked most successfully at a great height — above 20,000 feet — and sometimes forced his enemies down without firing a single shot. He earned the title of the Allies' King of the Air.

162. Captain George Guynemer, another great French ace, tried as a schoolboy to enlist in the infantry, but was declared too young and small. So he got work as a laborer in an aviation camp. The aviators taught him to fly and he soon became a pilot. He was an intrepid fighter and sometimes was in ten com-bats a day.

163. At first he led a charmed life, for he was forced several times to land in No Man's Land with his plane shot to pieces. But one day — after his fifty-third victory — he started in pursuit of a German plane and was seen fighting above Ypres. No more was heard of him. Even after the War, nothing could be learned of his fate.

164. Charles Nungesser was another of the great French aces, credited with 43 planes and balloons. He was badly injured several times, and once, in hospital, was offered a discharge and urged not to fly again. But he refused and returned on crutches to rejoin his regiment. He made many more flights.

165. The greatest American ace was Captain E. V. Rickenbacker, credited with 25 victories. He was an automobile racing driver and went to France as Pershing's chauffeur. There he entered the air service and soon became squadron commander. He was a fearless leader and never asked his men to do anything he would not do.

166. Frank Luke, with 18 planes to his credit, was the second American ace. He liked to hunt alone, and would seek out German planes far behind their lines. At last, while attacking three German balloons, he was attacked by ten German planes. He brought down two, and the three balloons, before he was himself killed.

167. Major Victor Raoul Lufberry was the third American ace. He was first a member of the Lafayette Escadrille, but joined our colors when we entered the war. His death occurred when his gas tank was ignited by fire from a German Fokker. Forced to jump, without a parachute, he was killed.

168. One of the distinguished air fighting forces was the Lafayette Escadrille, made up of Americans — among them Norman Prince, Bert Hall, Victor Chapman, Norman Hall, William Thaw and many other renowned fliers. They did great work in bringing down German planes and took part in many thrilling combats.

169. In 1918, on December 13, one of the record breaking flights began when a four-motored plane started out from London for Calcutta, India. The trip was one of great hardships, due partly to the many types of weather and climate through which the fliers were forced to go, but it was finally terminated successfully on January 16.

170. Hawker and Grieve, two Englishmen, tried to cross the Atlantic on May 16, 1919, from St. John's, Newfoundland. They soon ran into storms and had radiator trouble, and after flying 1,050 miles lighted in the ocean near a small steamer which rescued them. She had no radio, and for days they were thought lost.

171. The first air crossing of the Atlantic was accomplished by Lieutenant Commander Read in the navy flying boat, NC-4, when he went from Newfoundland by way of the Azores to Portugal. He had an exciting trip, with some narrow escape from catastrophe. He was of course acclaimed all over the world for his accomplishment.

172. The first non-stop flight was that of Lieutenant A. W. Brown and Captain John Alcock, of the British army who flew through fogs and clouds from Newfoundland to Ireland on June 14, 1919, in a little less than sixteen hours. They landed in a bog near a Marconi station, to the great astonishment of the operator.

173. On July 6, 1919, the first big dirigible ever seen in this country, the R-34, from England completed the first lighter-than-air non-stop crossing of the Atlantic. As the big ship soared over the Long Island field, Major Pritchard jumped with a parachute to the ground to give landing instructions. The flight took about 108 hours.

174. In November of the same year Captain Ross Smith started on a flight from London to Australia. He arrived safely about a month later. He said the worst part of the 11,000-mile trip was on the first day when it was so cold above Lyons, France, that his sandwiches froze solid. His route took him through Egypt, Persia and India.

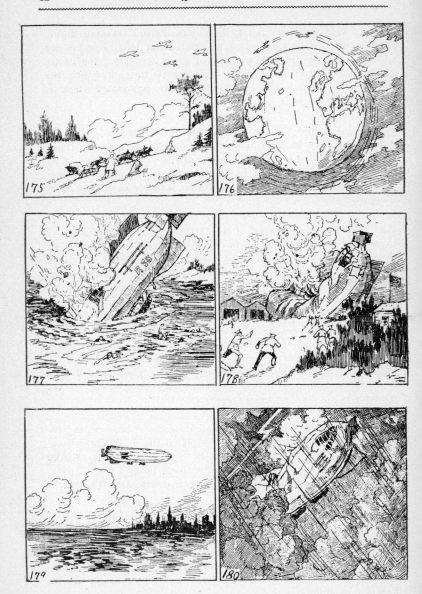

175. From July 15, to August 24, of 1920, four airplanes flew from New York City to Nome, Alaska. The Squadron was led by Lieutenant Street. They covered the distance of about 5,000 miles in fifty-five hours of actual flying time, with the usual thrilling experiences of long-distance flights, but without accident.

176. In the summer of 1924, was accomplished the first round-the world flight. Four American army airplanes started. One was wrecked against a mountainside in Alaska and one was forced down at sea. The other two returned in good shape, having circled the earth in flying time of 371 hours over a period of 175 days.

177. In August, 1921, a terrible calamity of the air occurred when the R-38, which the United states had bought from England, was destroyed over Hull, England, with the death of forty-four English and American officers and men. The dirigible fell into the river, where many of the men were drowned.

178. The next year — in February, 1922 — the Roma, bought from the Italian government by the United States, crashed to earth at Hampton Roads army base in Virginia, and burst into flame. Thirty-four men were killed. This catastrophe caused indignant criticism of the government for using hydrogen, instead of helium, in our dirigibles.

179. In October, 1924, the German dirigible, ZR-3, renamed the Los Angeles, was flown from Germany to Lakehurst, New Jersey, 5,066 miles, in about 81 hours. The airship was delivered to United States navy officials under the terms of the Versailles treaty. Leaving Germany on October 12, she reached Lakehurst on October 15.

180. The following year another United States navy dirigible, the giant Shenandoah, which had made some thrilling and successful flights, was wrecked by a severe storm over Ohio. Fourteen members of the crew were killed, including Commander Landsdowne. The survivors, some of them injured, had most harrowing experiences.

181. The English flier, Lieutenant Alan Cobham, left London November 16, 1925, and flew successfully, though with many exciting experiences, to Cape Town, South Africa. He was back in London in March, 1926, where he was received with enthusiasm for his feat having brought England in touch with another of her colonies.

182. Much of the exploration of the future will probably be done from airplanes. Byrd has already announced an exploration program that will occupy many years. In July, 1925, the Dr. A. Hamilton Rice expedition explored the headwaters of the Amazon and Lieutenant Walter Hinton flew a thousand miles over the jungle.

183. On May 9, 1926, Commander Richard Byrd, famous American flier, and Floyd Bennett flew from Spitzbergen to the North Pole and back in about fifteen hours. He saw no land. When he was over the pole he and Bennett shook hands, and then stood at attention in memory of the discoveror of the Pole, Commander Peary.

184. Two days later the Amundsen-Ellsworth-Nobile expedition in a semi-rigid dirigible, flew from the same place over the North Pole to Teller, Alaska. They encountered snow and fog, and when they landed they were entirely out of glue with which they had been mending holes in their ship caused by ice.

185. Early in May the Goodwill Flight of the United States army planes returned to the United States from their visit to South America. Though their trip had been marred by the fall of one of the planes and the death of its two occupants, the trip was successful in furthering understanding between the two Americas.

186. In April the Italian flier de Pinedo reached this country in his four-continent flight, having flown over Europe, Africa and South America. After an eventful time here — which included the burning of his plane at Roosevelt Dam — he again crossed the Atlantic and returned victoriously to Rome, where he was enthusiastically greeted.

For I dipt into the future, far as human eye could see.
Saw the vision of the world, and all the wonder that
    would be:
Saw the heavens fill with commerce, argosies of
    magic sails.
Pilots of the purple twilight, dropping down with
    costly bales:
Heard the heavens fill with shouting, and there rain'd
    a ghastly dew.
From nations' airy navies grappling in the central blue
Far along the world-wide, whisper of the south wind
    rushing warm;
With the standards of the people plunging thro' the
    thunder-storm:
Till the war-dream throbb'd no longer, and the battle-
    flags were furl'd
In the Parliament of man, the Federation of the world.

187. Early in May, 1927. the French war ace Nungesser, accompanied by Coli, started from Paris for New York, His plane, the White Bird, dropped its landing gears after it took off from Le Bourget Field to lighten its load. It was seen flying over Ireland. That was the last authentic report of the brave French fliers.

188. On May 20, and 21, the young American mail pilot, Charles Lindbergh, alone in his plane, the Spirit of St. Louis, flew from New York to Paris, through sleet and fog and rain, the first flier to accomplish that journey. This brilliant accomplishment by the flying ambassador did much to stimulate aviation.

189. The next big record was made by Clarence Chamberlain and Charles Levine when, on June 4, and 5, they flew from New York to Berlin — or nearly there, for they came down a little short of their goal, having lost their way and run out of gas. They broke the long-distance record which Lindbergh had established.

190. Next came the thrilling flight of Byrd — with Acosta, Balchen and Noville. Leaving New York with Paris as their goal they ran into bad weather at the start, and could not get away from it. When they finally dropped into the sea just off Ver-sur-Mer on July 1, they had proved that a plane can live through really terrific weather.

191.   In 1925, Commander Rodgers flew 1,992 miles from California toward Hawaii, when he was forced to land in the sea. On June 23, and 29, 1927, Maitland and Hegenberger made the first non-stop flight to the islands. A little later Smith and Bronte, though lost for hours in fog, landed in a tree in Hawaii with their last drop of gas gone.

192. And what of the future of flying? See the quotation from Tennyson's "Locksley Hall " on opposite page.

History of Air Mail

By HENRY C. RENOUF.

The history of aerial mail communication groups itself distinctly into three classes: pigeon post, balloon post, and the present airplane and airship post. Other types of more or less emergency means of aerial message carrying existed in many forms, but were never universally used. For instance, in 1474 in the Burgundian war the inhabitants of the beseiged city of Neuss placed messages in hollow cannon balls, and fired them over the hostile army to the camp of their rescuers. Pliny also tells us in his tenth Book that in the seige of a Roman fortress the garrison sent for help by releasing a swallow that had been brought there from its nest. There are also stories of bees having been used to carry messages, but the relatively short distance they can fly and the obvious difficulties encountered in handling a message made this of very limited usefulness.

The pigeon has been the bearer of messages real and symbolic since time immemorial. Good Father Noah, of the Ark, used a pigeon to discover whether the waters had yet receded, and the pigeon brought him the message of new life and cheer in the form of a green olive twig.

In the tenth and eleventh centuries the Sultans of Turkey used pigeon post very extensively, and it is chronicled that one Kalif was so fond of his little couriers he had a pet name for each one of the many dozens in his lofts. About this same time, in Egypt, 1288, Makrizi reports that there were almost 2,000 carrier pigeons in the service of the Imperial Court in Cairo. Even in more recent times part of the early success of the House of Rothchild can be attributed to the use of carrier pigeons which put the bankers in touch with market conditions long before their less resourceful competitors had any idea of what to expect.

Then in the seige of Paris carrier pigeons were used very extensively. It was comparatively easy to leave Paris by balloon, but quite impossible to return the same way. So pigeons were taken out of the city with the balloons, and held in the provinces in readiness to convey any important news back to Paris. Two other notable occasions of the use of carrier pigeons are the Great Barrier Island post of 1898, and the siege of Przemysl 1914-15. In the former case it was found almost impossible to navigate the thirty mile stretch of water between Barrier Island and New Zealand at certain seasons of the year, and pigeons were the only possible means of communicaton for weeks on end.

When in the beginning of this great War the town of Przemysl, Galicia (Austria) was beseiged without any communication for almost a year, pigeons were found to be the only fairly dependable means of getting news from the outside world, much as in the seige of Paris. This was probably the last extensive use of pigeons for mail carrying.

Carrier pigeons exist to this day, and, although their usefulness is more or less gone, they are probably more highly bred and efficient than ever, having been developed purely as a sport for racing or exhibition purposes.

The second stage of airmail history is practically limited to one occasion, namely, the seige of Paris, 1870-71. The city was completely cut off from all communication for four months, and when it became absolutely necessary to get in touch with the outside world, the use of balloons was hit upon. Two kinds were employed, one manned and carrying as much as 100 Kg. of mail and despatches as well as pigeons to return answers and important information, and the other made of wax paper about 25 to 30 ft. in diameter, unmanned, carrying perhaps 4 to 5 Kg. of postals. Ascents could only be made when the wind was favorable, as obviously, there were no means of guiding these balloons. Yet the majority of these flights were successful, and in the four month period between September 1870 and January 1871 about 2,500,000 letters, weighing approximately 11,0000 Kg. were safely transported over the German lines. Rates were 20 centimes for any part of France, but considerably more for foreign destinations. This was the first practical demonstration of the use of air mail on any large scale.

The carrying of aerial mail as done today, that is by powered airplanes or airships, was first inaugurated in India at the suggestion of an Englishman, Capt. Winham. On February

18th, 1911, this gentleman received permission from the postal authorities of Allahabad to arrange an aerial postal line between that city and a fair ground a few miles distant. The people at the fair were enthused with the idea and sent over 6,000 cards by airplane to the city. A Frenchman by the name of M. H. Piguet was the pilot.

The second honors for a mail flight of this kind go to Great Britain. This time, on the occasion of the coronation of King George V, in August 1911, about 130,000 pieces of mail were carried over a space of a few days between London and Windsor and return, by the Graham White Aviation Company.

Almost contemporaneously with this, a French flier by the name of Pierre Vedrines carried a bag of mail from Issy les Molineaux to Deauville, making the third postal flight in history. A year later the postal and military authorities co-operated in operating a line for a day, between Nancy and Luneville and still later, 1913, in opening a line between Paris and Bordeaux.

The fourth flight was made in Germany, also in August 1911, by pilot Hoffman carrying a bag of the "Berlin Morning Post" from Berlin to Frankfurt. This was a noteworthy flight, and of considerable length.

A month later, Sept. 25th — Oct. 1st, 1911, the United States made her first successful mail flights. Pilot Earl Ovington carried 43,247 pieces of mail between these dates from Garden City Estates to Mineola, Long Island a distance of twelve miles. Within the next two months seven other successful flights were made in the United States, four of which took place in the state of Georgia, viz: — Atlanta, Savannah, Columbus and Albany.

By 1914 a score of countries were running aerial lines, and several carrying mail and passengers, on a regular schedule system. In Europe particularly, distances were not great enough to make the aerial mail of any great general usefulness, and so relatively its growth was by no means as rapid as it was in this country. It was not until after the war however, that the United States really began developing its airways, and only a few years of effort put her far in the lead as far as aerial mail transportation was concerned. The trans-continental line to-day, equipped all the way with beacons for night flying has no parallel anywhere in the world.

Following are several countries that were pioneers in the development of air mail that have not as yet been mentioned:

Algiers, Feb. 1912, line Fez — Rabat.

Bavaria, Oct. 1912 and following, regular mail flights from Munich.

Belgium, May 2, 1913, special flight Brussels — Ghent.

Denmark, Sept. 2, 1911, flight Middleport — Fredericia by pilot Lvendsen.

Italy, Sept.—Oct. 1911, flights Bologna — Lido and Milan—Turin.

Japan, June 2, 1912, mail flight Yokahoma—Tokyo by American pilot Atwater.

Sweden, Aug. 29, 1912, special airmail edition of a newspaper was carried Stockholm—Upsala.

Switzerland, 1913, operated as many as 15 mail flights.

History of Pioneer Flights

NC-4

The successful crossing of the NC-4 from Newfoundland to Lisbon was the result of careful planning by the United States Navy, and the selection of the best material and men available. Three Navy Curtiss flying boats the NC-1, NC-3 and NC-4 under the command of John H. Towers were selected, and especially equipped with radios, lights and signalling devices. A line of destroyers was posted the entire distance from Trepassy to Lisbon for further assistance.

The three planes took the air from Trepassy, Newfoundland on May 16th, 1919, but only the NC-4 under the commond of Albert C. Read reached the Azores without mishap. After refuelling there he started for Lisbon May 27th and anchored in Lisbon harbor at eight the same evening. Three days later, May 30th, he started for Plymouth, England, arriving early in the afternoon of May 31st.

This flight is noteworthy as the first successful crossing of the Atlantic by air. No mail was carried as this was strictly a U. S. Navy enterprize.

NEWFOUNDLAND HAWKER

In response to the Daily Mail prize of 10,000 pounds for the first Trans-Atlantic flight, Messers Harry Hawker and McKensie Grieve started from St. Johns, Newfoundland for Ireland May 17, 1919 in a Sopwith biplane motored with 375 H. P. Rolls-Royce motor. After 14 hours, having traveled 1,200 miles their motor failed on account of trouble in the gas line, and they dropped into the sea near the Danish tramp steamer, "Mary," which picked them up May 18th, 1919.

As the rescuing steamer had no wireless aboard the fliers were thought lost for severel days until their arrival in England.

The "Mary" had not picked up their mail bag, which was salvaged a little later by an American boat near the scene of the accident. This mail was also brought to England.

The Post Office department in Newfoundland had expressely surcharged 200 of the 3c. caribou stamps for the occasion: "First Trans-Atlantic Air Post, April 1919." Eighteen of these over prints were faulty, and destroyed by the Postmaster. Of the remaining 182 copies, 95 were flown and 87 sold o. g. On account of the unfortunate ending of the flight most of these covers are water stained, and in many cases these stamps are restuck to the covers.

ALCOCK AND BROWN

Captain John Alcock and Lieut. Arthur Whitten Brown were the first to make a non-stop flight across the Atlantic, thereby capturing the Daily Mail Prize of 50,000 pounds. They left St. Johns, Newfoundland, June 14th, 1919 in a Vickers-Vimy bomber equipped with two 400 H. P. Rolls-Royce Eagle motors, and carrying 865 gallons of gasoline and 50 gallons of oil. The distance of 1,960 miles to Clifden, Ireland was covered in 16 hours 12 minutes. The fliers had dropped their undercarriage at the start to lighten their load and eliminate head resistance, so their landing in Ireland was a bit difficult, burying the nose of the plane in the mud and breaking the propeller.

Alcock and Brown continued their way to London in a sea plane. They were royally received here, and both Knighted by King George.

The regular 15c. 1897 Newfoundland stamp was surcharged: "Trans-Atlantic Air Post — 1919 — One Dollar" for any flights to take place after Hawker's attempt, and the covers carried by Alcock and Brown bear these stamps postmarked at St. Johns between June 10th and 13th and at London on June 18th.

R-34

Under the command of squadron leader G. H. Scott the British airship R-34 crossed the Atlantic between July 2nd and

4th, 1919, the first lighter-than-air craft to make this crossing. Leaving East Fortune, Scotland, on the morning of July 2, the R-34 finally reached her outdoor mooring in Roosevelt Field, Long Island, on the morning of July 6th, having covered the distance of 3,130 nautical miles in 108 hours. The return journey to Pulham, England took only 75 hours, although 200 miles longer, owing to favorable winds.

The R-34, equipped with five 250 H. P. Sunbeam motors, was 643 ft. long, 91 ft. high, and 79 ft. at the beam, with a gas capacity of 2,000,000 cubic feet. Her trip besides being the first crossing of any lighter-than-air craft was also the first return trip made by any type of aircraft.

A package of fourteen letters was carried, and for some reason unknown to the writer, was dropped overboard near the village of Selwar, Nova Scotia, where it was not found until November 8th, a period of four months having elapsed.

SIR ROSS SMITH

The first flight London to Australia, and also the longest flight ever made up to that time was accomplished by Sir Ross Smith November 12th — December 10th, 1919 in a Vickers-Vimy biplane equipped with two 400 H. P. Rolls Royce Eagle motors. The weight of the plane fully loaded with four men, 516 gallons of gas, 40 gallons of oil and 10 gallons of water as well as other necessities was over 5½ tons.

Of the four entrants in the competition to fly from England to Australia in 30 days Sir Ross Smith was the only formidable entrant and made the total distance of 11,500 miles just barely in time, taking 28 days. The trip took in Cairo, November 18th, Delhi November 23rd, Rangoon, Oceanica, Java, December 8th, and Port Darwin, Australia, December 10th.

ZR-3

The Zeppelin ZR-3, later rechristened the Los Angeles, was delivered to the United States under the treaty of Versailles as part of the German indemnity. The trip was begun Sunday,

October 12th, 1924 under the captaincy of Dr. Hugo Eckener, leaving Friedrichshafen at 6:37 A. M. and covering the distance of 5,066 miles to Lakehurst in 81 hours 17 minutes, ending Wednesday, October 15th at 9:25 A. M.,

The ship was the 126th built by the Zeppelin Co. and the largest up till then. Some of the specifications were: Length 200 meters; beam 28 meters; height 31 meters; gas capacity 70,000 cubic meters, contained in 14 separate compartments; power five 400 H. P., Maybach Motors.

About 16, 484 letters and postals were carried, destined almost entirely for the United States, with a few to Canada and 620 to South and Central America. Postal rates were 1M. for letters and 50 Pf. for cards.

AMUNDSEN—ELLSWORTH

The first airplane flight over the North Polar regions was conducted by Roald Amundsen and Lincoln Ellsworth during the months of May and June, 1925. Amundsen had attempted flight before but his planes were wrecked in testing out. It was his unbounded faith in the airplane as an aid to Polar explorations that decided Ellsworth to assist him in making the attempt.

The flight was started from Spitzbergen May 20th,, 1925 in two Dornier-Wal flying boats, the N-24 and N-25, powered with 450 H. P. Rolls Royce motors. Amundsen acted as observer in the N-25 and Ellsworth in the N-24. On May 22nd the N-25 was forced down by engine trouble in Lat. 87°44′ N. Long. 10°20′ W. approximately 136 nautical miles from the pole. The N-24 in attempting to land near the N-25 was badly crippled and the crew after some rather harrowing experiences, joined the crew of the N-25 on May 26. After considerable labor and several heart breaking attempts to fly, the N-25 was successfully launched into the air on June 15th and Amundsen classes this start as "amongst the most supreme in flying's history". The N-25 was again forced down in the sea near Nord Kap on Nordostland June 17th. The crew was rescued by the "Sjoliv" of Balsfjord late the same day and the N-25 towed to Kings Bay.

In connection with this flight there were issued subscription postals and those contributing to the expenses of the flight were given these postals. They were addressed to the Trans-Polar Flight Expedition, Christiania, Norway. On the reverse side was left a space for the name and address of the contributor in case the postal was desired to be returned after flight. The postals seen by us were franked on the reverse side with Norway stamps 5 ore (Scott's #104) and 25 ore (Scott's #126) and post-marked "King's Bay — May 18, 1925".

NORGE

Amundsen and Ellsworth in conjunction with Nobile of the Italian service made a successful flight over the North Pole during 1926 in the dirigible "Norge."

The Norge left Ciampino, Italy on April 10th, 1926 and flew by stages to Spitzbergen where on May 11th it left King's Bay. The Norge arrived at Teller, Alaska on May 13th, 1926 having flown over the Pole.

There were 91 covers carried on this flight from Ciampino, Italy. 31 of these bear the Postmark of departure, 60 of the covers having been turned in too late to receive this. 15 of the 60 covers, however, bear the postmark of the Ny-Alesund one of the last stopping places. All covers bear a special vignette and the arrival postmark of Teller, Alaska.

The next dirigible flight over the North Pole was made in 1928 by Nobile in the "Italia" which was subsequently wrecked and several lives lost. In passing it seems fit to mention the heroic sacrifice made by Amundsen in his endeavor to rescue the lost aviators.

DE PINEDO

When Commander Francisco de Pinedo left Rome on his "Round the World Flight" on April 23rd, 1925 in his "Savoia" seaplane, he had made no mention of carrying any mail. How-ever, upon arriving at Zamboanga, Philippines, August 19th he took all the mail, 292 letters, which was accumulated within the past few days for Manila, and left the next day. Thus the letters are all postmarked between the 17th and the 20th. At Cebu, an intermediary stop, de Pinedo picked up 732 more letters for Manila, postmarked between August 21st and 23. Then 10 letters were taken up at Atimonan and 34 at Corregidor and landed at Manila August 26th. All the letters received special arrival cachet in the form of a large aeroplane inscribed: "Via Pinedo's Flight Round the World, Manila, Philippine Islands, Aug. 26th, 1925."

From Manila de Pinedo carried 474 letters and cards to Aparri, the first stop on the way to Japan. They received a blue or black cancellation: "Comm. F. de Pinedo's — Airplane Savoia 1925 — Rome — Philippines — Tokyo."

═══════

DE PINEDO TRANS-ATLANTIC FLIGHT

After his return from the long flight to China and Japan of the previous year, de Pinedo fitted out a new twin motored seaplane, the Santa Maria, and started on February 8th, 1927 for America. Going via the west coast of Africa to the Cape Verde Islands he refuelled there, and started across the South Atlantic February 22nd covering the distance to Fernando to Noronha in about 12 hours. From there he turned south to Rio de Janeiro and Buenos Aires, and then flew straight up through the heart of South America to the Caribbean Sea, and then to Havana, Cuba. From Havana de Pinedo flew to New Orleans and further west as far as Roosevelt Dam, Arizona where unfortunately the the Santa Maria was burnt through the carelessness of a spectator who tossed a match into oily water near the plane.

A new plane however, the Santa Maria II, was sent over by the Italian Government and de Pinedo continued his trip on to New York where he remained for a week or so. In the middle of May he started for Newfoundland and on the 23rd took off from Trepassy for Rome via the Azores. After traveling 1,200 miles he was forced down at 33:54 W., 41:11 N. and towed to Fayal, the Azores, where the necessary repairs were made. This took a period of seven days, after which he flew back to where he had been forced down, landed in the water, and then took off again flying first to London and then to Rome via Lisbon.

The Post Office at St. John's, in honor of the flight, over-printed 300 of the 60c. black of the 1927 Cabot series in red in three lines: — "Air Mail — De Pinedo — 1927." De Pinedo carried with him 225 covers and these were cancelled at St. John's May 20th, Trepassy May 21st and Rome June 22nd. Of the remaining stamps, 20 mint copies were presented to the aviator, a small number were presented to Newfoundland Officials and some sold but never used.

PAN-AMERICAN FLIGHT

On December 21st, 1926, the five planes and men constituting the U. S. Army Pan American Good Will Flight started from Kelly Field, San Antonio, Texas under the command of Major Herbert A. Darque. The trip of over 22,000 miles carried the fliers through Central America, completely around the Continent of South America and back by the islands of the Caribbean, Cuba and Florida to Langley Field, Washington.

At Buenos Aires, half way through the trip, two of the planes collided in mid air resulting in the death of two fliers, the other two escaping serious injury by using their parachutes.

435 letters were carried, 80 which were lost in the accident.

LINDBERGH

The world has heard so much of the great flight of Charles A. Lindbergh that there is little use in giving more than the mere statistics of the event.

In the first place the enterprize was no doubt largely inspired by the $25,000.00 prize offered by Raymond Orteig for the first non-stop New York — Paris flight. Then it was made possible by the backing of a group of St. Louis men, namely: Harry Knight, Maj. William Robertson, Maj. Albert Lambert, J. D. Lambert, E. L. Ray,

Harry Knight, Harold Bixby and Earl Thompson, in honor of whose spirit the plane was named the "Spirit of St. Louis," a Ryan monoplane, span 46 feet, motored with a 200 H. P. Wright Whirlwind and equipped with a Pioneer earth inductor compass.

Starting from San Diego, California, May 9th, 1927, Lindbergh set out for St. Louis and covered the 1,600 miles in 14 hours 5 minutes. The next day he set out for New York covering the distance in 7 hours 15 minutes. At Curtiss and Roosevelt Fields two other planes were in readiness for the same flight, Byrd and Chamberlin. At the end of ten days, during which a few adjustments and tests were made, on the morning of May 20th the Spirit of St. Louis took the Air, and without any deviation from its course passed over Newfoundland, the coast of Ireland and reached Le Bourget Field, Paris, Saturday evening May 21st, having covered 3,610 miles in 33 hours 29 minutes. No mail was carried.

====

LINDBERGH'S TOUR OF U. S.

1927

July

20 New York City
20 Hartford, Conn.
21 Providence, R. I.
22 Boston, Mass.
23 Portland, Me.
25 Concord, N. H.
25 Old Orchard, Me.
26 Springfield, Vt.
27 Albany, N. Y.
28 Syracuse, N. Y.
28 Schenectady, N. Y.
29 Buffalo, N. Y.

August

1 Erie, Pa.
1 Cleveland, Ohio.
3 Pittsburgh, Pa.

4 Wheeling, W. Va.
5 Dayton, Ohio.
6 Cincinnati, Ohio.
8 Louisville, Ky.
9 Indianapolis, Ind.
10 Detroit, Mich.
12 Grand Rapids, Mich.
13 Chicago, Ill.
15 Springfield, Ill.
15 St. Louis, Mo.
17 Kansas City, Mo.
18 Wichita, Kans.
19 St. Joseph, Mo.
19 Moline, Ill.
19 Rock Island, Ill.
19 Davenport, Ia.
20 Milwaukee, Wis.
22 Madison, Wis.

23 Minneapolis, Minn.
23 St. Paul, Minn.
25 Little Falls, Minn.
25 Fargo, N. D.
27 Sioux Falls, S. Dak.
27 Sioux City, Ia.
29 Des Moines, Iowa.
30 Omaha, Nebr.
31 Denver, Colo.

September

1 Pierre, S. Dak.
2 Cheyenne, Wyo.
3 Salt Lake City Utah,
4 Boise, Idaho.
5 Butte, Mont.

At this point he left his plane and went for a weeks vacation in Northern Montana.

12 Spokane, Wash.
13 Seattle, Wash.
14 Portland, Oregon.
16 San Francisco, Calif.
17 Oakland, Calif.
17 Sacramento, Calif.
19 Reno, Nevada.
20 Los Angeles, Calif.
21 San Diego, Calif.
23 Tucson, Arizona.

24 Lordsburgh, N. Mex.
24 El Paso, Texas.
25 Sante Fe, N. Mex.
26 Abilene, Tex.
26 Ft. Worth, Tex.
27 Dallas, Tex.
28 Oklahoma City, Okla.
30 Tulsa, Okla.

October

1 Muskogee, Okla.
1 Little Rock, Ark.
3 Memphis, Tenn.
5 Chattanooga, Tenn.
5 Birmingham, Ala.
7 Jackson, Miss.
8 New Orleans, La.
10 Jacksonville, Fla.
11 Atlanta, Ga.
12 Spartanburgh, S. C.
14 Winston-Salem, N. C.
15 Richmond, Va.
17 Washington, D. C.
18 Baltimore, Md.
19 Atlantic City, N. J.
21 Wilmington, Del.
22 Philadelphia, Pa.
23 New York City.

LINDBERGH'S SOUTHERN TOUR

1927

December

13 Washington, D. C.
14 Mexico City.

28 Guatemala City.
30 Belize, Brit. Honduras.

1928

January

1 San Salvador.
3 Tegucigalpa, Honduras.
5 Managua, Nicaragua.
7 San Jose, Costa Rica.
9 Panama City.
11 Balboa, Canal Zone.
12 Colon.
26 Cartagena, Columbia.

27 Bogota, Columbia.
29 Maracay, Venezuela.
30 Caracas, Venezuela.
31 St. Thomas, Virgin Is.

February

2 San Juan, Porto Rico.
4 Santo Domingo.
6 Port au Prince, Haiti.
8 Havana, Cuba.

LINDBERGH'S RETURN TO U. S.

13 St. Louis, Mo.
20 Springfield, Ill.
20 Peoria, Ill.
20 Chicago, Ill.

21 Peoria, Ill.
21 Springfield, Ill.
21 St. Louis, Mo.

CHAMBERLIN

In the spring of 1927 there were as many as a half dozen aspirants at Curtis Field, Long Island for the first New York to Europe non-stop trans-Atlantic crossing. These finally boiled down to three definite contestants, Lindbergh, Chamberlin and Byrd, Lieut. Commander Davis and Lieut. Stanton Wooster, notable entrants for the flight, having been killed in their Fokker tri-motored monoplane the American Legion, April 26th, in a test flight. It seemed for weeks, before Lindbergh "came out of the west" as if Chamberlin would be the first one to make the attempt, and the sturdy Bellanca monoplane, Columbia, was in readiness long before its final start waiting for favorable weather, and the settlement of wranglings on the part of its owner.

Originally Bertaud, who later was lost with J. D. Hill in the Old Glory on her attempted flight to Rome, was to act as co-pilot. His temperament, however, did not agree with Levine's, and for days no one knew who would be the second man on the trip. At last on the morning of June 4th, 1927, the world was startled by the announcement that Levine himself had started for Europe with Chamberlin.

The Columbia headed for Berlin and although it failed in reaching its destination, being forced down at Eisleben, Germany, it covered a distance of 3,905 miles in about 42 hours, establishing the world's long distance record.

No official mail was carried on this flight, although there was some notoriety about mail being stamped without authorization by a Long Island Postmaster.

RICHARD BYRD

After having flown over the North Pole in the spring of 1926 Commander Byrd prepared for greater adventure the following spring by preparing to fly the Atlantic. He was backed in this enterprize by Rodman Wanamaker. The Fokker monoplane America motored with three 200 H. P. Wright Whirlwind engines was especially built for the flight, and carried besides Byrd three other fliers, Noville, Acosta and Bernt Balchen.

The "America" left Roosevelt Field in the early morning of June 29th, 1927 flying for Paris. Heavy fogs between Paris and the coast prevented a safe landing and finally after 42 hours the fliers were forced down in the sea by Ver-sur-Mer having actually spanned a distance of 3,477 miles, but having probably covered closer to 4,000 miles.

Byrd carried 50 letters on the flight bearing the official New York departure cachets June 21st and Ver-sur-Mer arrival cachets July 3rd.

MAITLAND AND HEGENBERGER

After the successful Atlantic crossings of Lindbergh and Chamberlin within a fortnight of each other, speculation arose as to the plausibility of a Pacific flight, and the U. S. army Air Corps was the first to put this to a test. Lieutenants Lester J. Maitland and Albert F. Hegenberger were chosen to make the attempt in a tri-motored Fokker monoplane equipped with the most modern instruments and assisted by a new development, the radio beacon.

The morning of June 28th, 1927 saw the start from the Municipal Airport of Oakland, California at 7:09 A. M. The distance of 2,400 miles of water was covered in 25 hours 50 minutes, establishing a world's record for uninterrupted ocean flight.

No mail was carried.

SMITH AND BRONTE

The second Pacific crossing and the first crossing by civilians was made July 14th, 1927 by Ernest L. Smith and Emory Bronte in a Travel Air monoplane, the "City of Oakland" powered with a 200 H. P. Wright Whirlwind motor. They covered a distance of 2,340 milese in 25 hours 36 minutes, landing on the Island of Molokai just as their gasoline was exhausted. They were forced to wreck their plane in landing.

As these gentlemen did not fly in time stipulated by the Dole Race regulations they did not receive the prize money which was awarded later to Arthur Goebel and Lieut. William Davis, Jr., 1st prize $25,000., and Martin Jensen and Paul Schluter 2nd prize $10,000.

No official mail was carried on any of these flights.

BROCK AND SCHLEE

The planned Round the World flight of Edward F. Schlee, Detroit business man, and William S. Brock, pilot, was largely undertaken to demonstrate that it was both possible and practical to circle the globe by air without advance preparation in less than 28 days, the record time made by the U. S. Round-the-World Fliers.

They started from Harbor Grace, Newfoundland on August 27th, in their single 200 H. P. Wright Whirlwind motored Stinson-Detroiter monoplane, the Pride of Detroit, and covered the first lap of 2,350 miles to Plymouth, England in 23 hours. Only stopping to refuel, the Pride of Detroit flew successfully over

Europe, India, China and to Japan in a space of 18 days or a total flying time of 145½ hours. The Public sentiment was so strong against a continuation of the flight across the Pacific that the fliers finally abandoned their trip, and sailed for the U. S. by steamer.

No official mail was carried.

SOUTHERN CROSS

Captain Kingsford-Smith and his three companions, Keith V. Anredson, co-pilot, Charles P. T. Ulm, and William A. Todd, navigators took off from Oakland airport, California in their tri-motored Fokker, Southern Cross in May, 1928 for Sidney, Australia a distance of about 9,000 miles. The first leg of the flight was to Honolulu then to Fiji Islands, then Brisbane and finally Sidney.

The flight was backed by the Government of New South Wales, and had the support of the U. S. Post Office Department, authorizing the carrying of 1,500 letters. Postal rates were 5c. for the first ounce and 3c. for each additional ounce.

BREMEN

The flight of the Bremen on April 12th and 13th, 1928 from Baldonnel Airdrome, Ireland to Greenly Island, Labrador a distance of 2,125 miles was the first non-stop East to West crossing of the Atlantic by an airplane. The Bremen was an all-metal single 300 H. P. Junkers motored and Junkers made monoplane. Baron Gunther von Huenefeldt, the publicity agent of the German Luft Hausa, was the backer of the expedition, and came along as passenger on the trip. Captain Herman Koehl was pilot, and the Irish Captain James Fitzmaurice acted as co-pilot. The fliers became hopelessly lost over Labrador on account of fog, and after 36½ hours flying, landed on the only clear spot they could find near the light tower on Greenly Island.

On account of the inaccessibility of the place the Bremen was thought lost for several days and even after it was located it took a week for help to reach there. The first man to reach

Greenly Island was Duke Schiller in a Fairchild Monoplane especially equipped with skiis. No official mail was carried.

GRAF ZEPPELIN

The flight of the L-127, named the Graf Zeppelin, was the first of its kind ever made commercially, the previous flight of the British R-34 and the German LZ-126 or ZR-3 being made for their respective governments. The airship left Friedrichshafen(Germany at 7:50 a. m. October 11, 1928, and after 112 hours in the air landed at Lakehurst, N. J. October 14 at about 5 p. m. The distance covered was approximately 6,000 miles, the result of a round-about course taken towards the south due to unfavorable weather.

General specifications of the Graf Zeppelin are: Length 770 ft.; height 116 ft.; length of main gondola 98 ft.; cubic capacity 344,487 ft.; power plant 5 Maybach motors of 530 H. P. each; fuel about 106,000 cubic ft. of "blau" gas; crew 40 men including officers; estimated cost between $1,200,000 and $1,500,000.

Dr. Hugo Eckener, the commander, had also piloted the ZR-3 from Friedrichshafen in 1924, and is considered by many the world's foremost airship pilot. He had twenty passengers on this flight including Lt. Comm. Rosendahl U.S.N., commander of the Los Angeles, Col. Herrera of the Spanish Air Service, Count Brandenstein, son-in-law of the late Count Zeppelin, and one woman, Lady Drummond Hay, a newspaper writer.

Mail was carried on this flight for which the German Post Office issued special stamps in 2 m. and 4 m. denominations, the former being used for post cards and the latter for letters. One bag of mail was dropped en route at the German Consulate at Madeira, but the majority of the mail was destined for this country.

The mail carried on the initial trip consisted of approximately 70,000 pieces, 40 thousand postal cards and 30 thousand letters. On the return trip 101,683 pieces of mail was carried, 49,745 letters and 51,938 postcards.

A Catalogue

of

AIR MAIL STAMPS

and

HISTORICAL COVERS

Compiled and Edited by

KALENIK LISSIUK *and* JOHN W. NICKLIN

IMPORTANT NOTICE.

You will note that the arrangement of the Historical Air Mail is in many ways different from other catalogues.

First, there is found following the description of each stamp, a letter such as "a" or "b". This refers to the cut or design of the particular stamp and corresponds to a simularly labeled cut in the text above.

In describing perforations we have employed the symbol + instead of the fractions ordinarily used. Hence 13+ means more than 13 but less than 14 guage.

Instead of the costomary two columns of figures found in most catalogues, there are three to be found. The first gives the price for unused, the second for used, while the third prices the stamp on cover.

The first or unused condition requires no comment. In the second the ordinary cancelled copy is considered without particular reference to its method of use. The third column prices the stamp on a flown cover — any flown cover. It is of course understood that first flight or special flights may be more valuable than the normal cover.

Following the stamp description you will note a figure in parenthesis. This indicates the number of stamps issued of the variety. We point out that complete information as to the number of stamps issued is not always given. We should appreciate such assistance as our readers can be to us in supplying this deficiency. Kindly advise us as to source of your information so that a proper notation thereof may be made in our records.

The section covering Historical Flights will we believe, be of much interest and value to collectors.

Constant amplification, revision and correction will be attempted on the subject matter for inclusion in the 1930 edition. We invite you all to join in this work. Kindly remember that the Historical Air Mail Catalogue is issued for, and in a large measure, by the Aero Philatelists of America.

New Issues of Air Mail Stamps: In still another way is the fullest co-operation of our public desired. This is in the reporting and giving any information of newly issued air mail stamps. We will of course, have to rely on our foreign readers to supplement and confirm the information furnished us by our regular correspondents throughout the world. In reporting new issues give date of issue, number issued and any other particulars which you think may be of interest.

It is our hope that we can shortly make arrangements for getting this new information before you in a systematic and attractive way. Just what form the publication of this news will take we must leave for the future to decide.

K. Lissiuk Philatelic Co., Inc.

UNITED STATES.

Mail flights were attempted as early as 1910 when plans were made to drop a bag of mail on the deck of the U. S. S. Pennsylvania, but this was prevented by an accident. However, between Sept. 23rd and Oct. 1st, 1911, nearly 45,000 pieces of mail were carried by plane between Garden City Estates and Mineola, Long Island, making the first aerial mail in the United States.

Official government flights nevertheless were not carried out for several years, and no regular air routes existed until May 15th, 1918 when the line was opened between Washington — Philadelphia — New York, and the first series of air stamps was issued.

August 21st, 1923, marked the opening of the first New York—San Francisco line, but the distance Chicago' — Cheyenne was made by rail on account of darkness. However this difficulty was overcome in the following year by erecting beacons and building 34 emergency landing fields along the route.

Original postal rates were:

New York — Chicago	6 cents
New York — Cheyenne	16 cents
New York—San Francisco	24 cents

On July 1st, 1924 the completed New York — San Francisco Transcontinental line was opened, and on that day were carried approximately 20,000 pieces of mail, necessitating the use of two planes. The distance of 2680 miles was covered in about 30 hours. The stops on this route are: New York, Bellefont, Cleveland, Chicago,' Iowa City, Omaha, Cheyenne, Rawlins, Rock Springs, Salt Lake City, Elko, Reno, San Francisco.

After Aug. 31st, 1927 all air lines the government had established were operated under contract by private concerns. The first lines to be taken over were the Cleveland — Detroit and Chicago — Detroit lines known as C. A. M. Routes 6 and 7 which the Ford Motor Company contracted for using their metal Ford — Stout monoplanes, motored with 400 H. P. Liberty engines.

1919 (Aug. 14)

Aeromarine flying boat dropped a bag of mail on the forward deck of the White Star Liner "Adriatic" 1½ hours after she had left New York.

1927 (June 18)

Lindbergh 10c blue stamp placed on sale.

5,707,000 first issue.
2,500,000 second issue.

1927 (January 25)

20c Airmail stamp placed on sale.

1927 (August 1)

Chamberlin took off from special runaway on board S. S. Leviathan with bag of mail and flew to Teterboro, New Jersey.

1928 (May 26)

10c stamp first sold in booklet form.

1918 (May 15)

No watermark.		Perforated 11.	
1 6c orange	.50	.30	.60
2 16c green	.70	.40	.80
3 24c carmine & blue	.90	.60	1.10
3a. Centre inverted.	(100) 1,250.00	—	—

1923

No watermark.   Perforated 11.
4   8c dark green   .30   .20   .35
5   16c deep blue   .35   .20   .40
6   24c carmine   .50   .30   .60

1926-27

No watermark.   Perforated 11.
7   10c deep blue   .25   .15   .20
8   15c sepia   .40   .25   .50
9   20c light green   .40   .20   .55

1927

No watermark.   Perforated 11.
10 10c deep blue (Lindbergh
        airmail)   .20   .10   .15

1928

No watermark.   Perforated 11.
11 5c carmine & blue   .10   .05   .10

ALAOUITES.

Aerial transportation was first employed in the winter of 1924-25 when several French military planes flew on schedule between Latakia and Homs carrying both mail and passangers. Syria, also under French mandate, had been operating lines since 1920, and had actually covered the route Latokia — Homs previously.

1925 (Jan. 1)      Perforated 14, 13+.

Overprinted.
French Stamps of
1900-20

"a"

1   2pi on 40c red & light blue *"a"* (16,000) .95 .95 1.25

2   3pi on 60c violet & ultramarine "*a*" (16,000) .95 .95 1.25
3   5pi on 1fr claret & olive bistre "*a*" (16,000) .95 95 1.25
4 10pi on 2fr orange & light blue "*a*"(16,000) .95 95 1.25

1925 (March 1)   **AVION**

                                              Perforated 13+.

   Overprinted in green
   on Stamps of Syria.

ﻃﻴ
"*b*"

5   2pi brown "*b*"   .20 .15 .20
    5a. Red overprint.   —   —   —
6   3pi brownish orange "*b*"   .25 .20 .25
    6a. Overprint inverted (Avion on right) —   —   —
7   5pi violet "*b*"   .35 .30 .40
    7a. Overprint inverted (Avion on right) —   —   —
    7b. Red overprint.   —   —   —
8 10pi brownish violet "*b*"   .65 .60 .80
    8a. Overprint inverted (Avion on right) —   —   —
    8b. Red overprint.   —   —   —

1926   Perforated 13+.
  Alaouites First Issue
  Overprinted Airplane.
    in red.
"*c*"

 9   2pi brown "*c*"   .10 .10 .12
10   3pi brownish orange "*c*"   .12 .10 .15
11   5pi violet "*c*"   .15 .12 .20
12 10pi brownish violet "*c*"   .35 .30 .45

ALBANIA.

Arrangements were made in 1924 with the German Aero Lloyd A.-G. to inaugurate an aerial service in Albania, and a series of seven stamps was issued in February of the following year by the Imperial Printing Office of Berlin. These stamps were available to dealers in Berlin, where the German Aero Lloyd offered them for sale. They were first used on May 30th, 1925 between Tirana and Avlona and received special departure and arrival cachets: — "Tirane — Posta Aerore—date," "Vlone — Posta Aerore — date." Between 900 and 1000 covers are believed to have been flown on this first trip.

On the following day, June 1st, a special flight from Tirana to Scutari and Tirana to Koritza took place for the benefit of the Albanian Red Cross. Special envelopes were used with the usual departure and arrival cachets which are in use today. Only 250 letters were carried bearing stamps overprinted with a Geneva Cross besides the air stamps.

1925

Watermarked
Lozenges.

Perforated 14.

"a"

1	5q light green "a"	(150,000)	.08	.05	.10
2	10q red "a"	(150,000)	.12	.10	.25
3	25q dark blue "a"	(150,000)	.25	.20	.35
4	50q green "a"	(150,000)	.45	.40	.65
5	1fr deep violet & black "a"	(100,000)	.80	.75	2.00
6	2fr greenish olive & violet "a"	(75,000)	1.00	1.50	3.00
7	3fr orange brown & green "a"	(50,000)	2.50	2.40	4.00

1927 (Jan. 18)   *Rep. Shqiptare*   Overprinted on Abanian
Stamps of 1925

"*b*"

8	5q light green "*b*"	(55,000)	.10	.10	.15
9	10q red "*b*"	(55,000)	.15	.12	.25
	9a. Overprint inverted.	(100)	—	—	—
10	25q dark blue "*b*"	(58,000)	.25	.22	.40
11	50q green "*b*"	(78,100)	.50	.45	.70
12	1fr deep violet & black "*b*"	(72,000)	.70	.65	.90
	12a Overprint inverted.	(50)	—	—	—
13	2fr greenish olive & violet "*b*"	(48,450)	1,10	1.00	1.50
14	3fr orange brown & green "*b*"	(22,200)	2.50	2.25	3.75

1928

Overprinted on
Albania Stamps
of 1925.

"*c*"

15	5q light green "*c*"	(16,375)	1.00	1.25	—
16	10q red "*c*"	(14,600)	1.25	1.50	—
17	25q dark blue "*c*"	(23,075)	1.00	1.25	—
18	50q green "*c*"	(13,040)	1.50	2.00	—
19	1fr deep violet & black "*c*"	(5,500)	2.25	3.00	—
20	2fr greenish olive & violet "*c*"	(5,350)	2.25	3.00	—
21	3fr orange brown & green "*c*"	(5,350)	2.25	3.00	—

ARGENTINE.

The first flights in the Argentine were made in the
fall of 1912 by the military authorities around Rosario in
a campaign to promote aviation. Unofficial stamps of
5 centavos were printed and actually sold over the post

office counter, the proceeds going to a fund for new planes.

The first regular postal flight occurred on September 2nd, 1917 when 157 letters were carried from Buenos Aires to Montevideo using regular stamps of Argentine. A special round cachet was applied "First International Air Mail between Buenos Aires and Montevideo piloted by Teodero Fels Sept. 2, 1917."

In 1924 a line was started between Buenos Aires and Montevideo which ran three months and was then suspended for want of a government subsidy.

In 1925 four or five lines were operated between Buenos Aires — Mendoza; between Cordoba — Villa Dolores; between Buenos Aires — Rio de Jeneiro; between Cordoba — Rio Cuarto. All these flights employed ordinary postage with special cachets.

The first set of regular airmail stamps was issued in February 1928, and covers received a cachet "Buenos Aires — Vici Aereo — 29 February 1928." The 18c and 36c were sold out in a very short time. This set was issued for the Trans-Atlantic mail service between Buenos Aires and Toulouse, France.

1928

Watermark R. A. in Sun.   Perforated 13+.

"*a*"   "*b*"

"*c*"   "*d*"

```
 1   5c red "a"                    (80,000)   .15   .20   —
 2  10c metallic blue "a"          (80,000)   .15   .20   —
 3  15c brown "b"                 (200,000)   .20   .25   —
 4  18c grayish lilac "a"          (30,000)  1.50  1.50   —
 5  20c ultramarine "b"           (100,000)   .30   .40   —
 6  24c dark blue "b"                         .30   .45   —
 7  25c violet "c"                (200,000)   .35   .45   —
 8  30c bright red "c"            (300,000)   .45   .50   —
 9  35c rose "d"                  (300,000)   .45   .50   —
10  36c light brown "a"           (30,000)   1.50  1.50   —
11  50c grayish black "d"         (500,000)   .70   .80   —
12  54c chocolate "b"             (100,000)   .80  1.00   —
13  72c yellow green "b"           (50,000)  1.20  1.50   —
14  90c dark brown "c"            (100,000)  1.20  1.50   —
15  1 peso dull blue & red "c"     (50,000)  2.00  2.50   —
16  1.08p rose & deep blue "c"    (100,000)  2.00  2.50   —
17  1.26p dark violet&green "d"   (100,000)  2.25  2.75   —
18  1.80p blue & rose lilac "d"   (100,000)  3.00  3.50   —
19  3.60p gray & blue "d"          (50,000)  6.00  7.00   —
```

=====

AUSTRIA.

Austria's first aerial postal services date from 1910 when the balloon post was installed. No stamps were issued, but ocassionally special cards marked for unusual events such as the International Aviation Exhibition at Vienna in 1912. During the war military aeroplane service superceded all private attempts, lasting until March 30th, 1918 when the first official air line was opened, Vienna — Krakau — Lemberg and return. The stamps used were of the regular issue of the monarchy surcharged "Flugpost" and values.

In 1922 under the new Republic the first special air stamp came out, and a line was started between Vienna — Prague — Warsaw — Strassburg — Paris.

1918 (March 30)

Austrian Stamps
Overprinted.

No watermark.

Perforated 12+.

"*a*"

1	1.50k on 2k lilac "*a*"		.12	.12	.18
2	2.50k on 3k dull yellow brown		.15	.15	.25
	2a. Inverted overprint (white paper) (100)		60.00	—	—
3	4k light gray		.55	.55	.75

There were two printings of this set, one
in 1916 and one in 1918. The former was
on gray paper and is quite scarce mint, while
the latter was on white paper and is seldom
seen on cover.

1922 (Oct. 31)

No watermark.

Perforated 12+.

"*b*"   "*c*"

4	300k claret "*b*"	(525,000)	.20	.15	.25
5	400k deep green "*b*"	(287,000)	.40	.35	.45
6	600k bistre "*b*"	(816,000)	.10	.08	.15
7	900k orange brown "*b*"	(821,000)	.10	.08	.15
8	1200k violet brown "*c*"	(810,000)	.10	.08	.15
9	2400k bluish gray "*c*"	(812,000)	.20	.18	.30
10	3000k dark brown "*c*"	(570,000)	.40	.35	.60
11	4800k deep blue "*c*"	(567,000)	.55	.50	.75

No. 5, 400k green, was not issued until
April 22nd, 1924.

1925 (Aug. 1)

No watermark
Typographed.

Perforated 12, 13.

"*d*"   "*e*"

12	2g brownish gray "*d*"	.02	.02	.05
13	5g crimson "*d*"	.02	.02	.05
14	6g blue "*d*"	.04	.04	.10
15	8g light green "*d*"	.05	.04	.10
16	10g reddish orange "*e*"	.10	.08	.15
17	15g claret "*e*"	.15	.12	20
18	30g violet brown "*e*"	.30	.26	.35
19	50g black "*e*"	.50	.45	.60
20	1s blue "*e*"	.35	.30	.45
21	2s deep green "*e*"	.70	.60	.90

1926 (Sept. 7)

No watermark
Typographed.

Perforated 12, 13.

22	10g orange "*d*"	.03	.02	.05
23	15g violet red "*d*"	.05	.04	.10
24	30g bistre "*d*"	.10	.08	.12
25	50g slate "*d*"	.17	.15	.20
26	3s red brown "*e*"	1.00	.85	1.10
27	5s dark blue "*e*"	1.50	1.40	1.75
28	10s intense brown, gray "*e*"	3.00	2.75	3.50

BOLIVIA.

The first set of stamps was issued in 1914 to commemorate the opening of the National Aviation School. Lines were established between Sucre — Oruro — La Paz, but the stamps were available for ordinary postage up to the time these lines were inaugurated. The following year, 1925, regular issue Bolivia 50c orange of 1919-1921 was surcharged for Sucre, Oruro or La Paz semiofficially, and used for one or two special flights.

1924

No watermark.

Perforated 14.

"*b*"   "*c*"

1	10c deep red & black "*a*"	(225,000)	.35	.35	1.00
2	15c carmine & black "*a*"	(150,000)	.45	.45	1.00
3	25c blue & black "*a*"	(100,000)	.55	.55	1.25
4	50c orange & black "*a*"	(80,000)	1.00	1.00	1.50
5	1b red brown & black "*b*"	(50,000)	1.85	1.85	2.50
6	2b dark brown & black "*b*"	(20,000)	3.50	3.50	4.50
7	5b violet & black "*b*"	(10,000)	8,00	8.00	10.00

BRAZIL.

Brazil appropriated almost $25,000,000 in the fall of 1919 for aviation, but made nothing out of it for five or six years following. In 1925, several private flights were made for survey purposes carrying mail incidentally, usually by foreign concerns. In March, 1927, a schedule line was established between Porto Alegre — Pelotas— Ria Grande by a German company who sold out their rights to a native concern three months later. The official set of air stamps was printed for thsi route.

1927

| Brazil Official Stamp of 1923 Overprinted "Service Aero" and values. | SERVIÇO AÉREO 200 Rs. "a" | Perforated 12. No watermark. |

1	50r on 10r dull gray & black "a"	.10	.10	.20
2	200r on 100r brown & black "a"	.15	.18	.25
3	200r on 2000r reddish brown & black "a"	6.00	6.50	8.00
4	200r on 5000r brown & black "a"	.15	.18	.25
5	300r on 500r orange & black "a"	.20	.25	.35
6	300r on 600r violet & black "a"	.20	.25	.35
7	500r on 50r gray & black "a"	.35	.40	.60
8	1000r on 20r greenish olive & black "a"	.60	.80	1.00
9	2000r on 100r vermilion & black "a"	1.10	1.25	1.75
10	2000r on 200r deep blue & black "a"	1.10	1.25	1.75
11	2000r on 10000r black "a"	1.10	1.25	1.75
12	5000r on 20000r blue & black "a"	1.75	2.25	3.00
13	5000r on 50000r green & black "a"	1.75	2.25	3.00
14	5000r on 100000r red orange & black "a"	3.00	4.25	5.00
15	10000r on 500000r brown & black "a"	5.50	6.50	8.00
16	10000r on 1000000r deep brown & black "a"	5.50	6.50	8.00

BULGARIA.

Lines between Sofia — Roussa—Varna were opened November 8th, 1927, and an issue of two stamps was put on sale. However, all mail was additionally taxed; 4L if registered letter, 2L if plain letter and 1_ if post card. All covers received special cachets on the first flight, bearing the name of the town, date and first flight. These cachets were destroyed afterwards.

These lines were operated by a German company which in return received a large percentage of the stamps from the government. Many of these of course, were sold in Germany direct to stamp dealers.

1927
Bulgarian Issue 1925-28
    Overprinted in
    various colors.
    No watermark.

Perforated 11+.

1	1L on 6L blue & lemon yellow	(100,000)	.04	.03	.06
	1a. Overprint inverted. (200)	—	—	—
2	2L olive	(200,000)	.12	.08	.15
3	4L dark lake & yellow	(100,000)	.25	.20	.35
4	10L brownish black & orange brown		.60	.45	.75

CANADA.

Though various private airmail stamps have been in use in Canada for a number of years, the first government issue did not appear until September, 1928. The stamp is beautiful in conception and splendidly executed.

1928 (Oct. 3)

    No watermark.

Perforated 12.

"a"

| 1 | 5c olive brown *"a"* | .10 | .08 | .12 |

CHILE.

A set of five stamps was issued in May, 1927 for the opening of the line Valpariso — Santiago and return. These stamps were not sold mint due to the limited number issued but were directly affixed to the covers offered for transportation by air mail. Hence their rarity unused.

It is stated on the authority of the Chilean Post Office that these stamps are not official. They are issued by the commercial aviation company operating the line and represent a fee collected by that company for letters carried by their planes. Due to the circumstances of their issue, they are omitted from this catalogue.

In 1928 was issued an undoubtedly official set which we list below.

1928

Regular Stamps of Chile 1925-28
Overprinted in blue,
Black or red.

Perforated.

"*a*"　　　　　　　"*b*"

1 20c black & orange brown
　　　(black) "*a*"　　　　　　(150,000)　—　—　—
2 25c black & dark blue
　　　(red) "*a*"　　　　　　(150,000)　—　—　—
3 30c brown & black(black)"*a*"(150,000)　—　—　—
4 40c black & deep violet
　　　(red) "*a*"　　　　　　(150,000)　—　—　—
5 50c black & green (red) "*a*" (150,000)　—　—　—
6 1p black & green (blue) "*a*" (150,000)　—　—　—

7 2p black & vermilion
       (blue) "*a*"   (150,000)   — — —
8 3p on 5c dark blue (red) "*b*" (150,000)   — — —
9 5p black & greenish olive
       (blue) "*a*"   (100,000)   — — —
10 6p on 10c black & dark blue
       (red) "*b*"   (150,000)   — — —
11 10p black & yellow (blue)"*a*" (75,000)   — — —

CHINA.

The first experimental mail flight was attempted on May 7th, 1920, between Tientsin and Pekin, and successfully completed. Only a very limited number of letters was carried and stamped in the ordinary way plus special additional departure and arrival cachets. These covers are very rare.

Regular air stamps were issued July 1st, 1921 for the Pekin — Tsinanfu line, and about a dozen flights actually made up to Sept. 23rd, 1921, when operations ceased, and the stamps were withdrawn from sale. On August 4th of the following year, 1922, another line Pekin — Peitaiho was opened and operated until Sept. 11th during which time the air stamps were offered for sale. Their last appearance was between May 23rd and Sept. 30th, 1923 for the line Pekin — Tientsin. Covers of the first period of 1921 are much scarcer than the subsequent ones.

In 1924 a semi private line was operated between Mukden and Newchang in Manchuria, for which a series of private stamps was printed, 15c green, 30c red, and 45c violet. These were used only a very short time.

In 1925, Sept. 12th, the Italian aviator de Pinedo flew from Shanghai to Tokyo, Japan, and carried 50 covers with him. These were stamped with a current 3c stamp but received a special cachet, "First Airmail —China — Japan."

1921 Perforated 12.

No watermark

"*a*"

1 15c bluish green & black "*a*"   .40 .50 .80
2 30c scarlet & black "*a*"   .70 1.00 1.50
3 45c deep violet & black "*a*"   1.00 1.50 2.00
4 60c blue & black "*a*"   1.50 2.25 3.50
5 90c greenish olive & black "*a*"   2.85 4.00 5.50

Shortly after the Nationalist forces entered Pekin in 1928, a limited number of the Air Mail Stamps of 1921 remaining in official hands were placed on sale. Reports have stated that these were from a new printing. We are definately assured from reliable sources that this is not the case. At all events those received by us were in original packages dated 1921. We believe prices for these popular stamps are bound to advance.

CILICIA.

An aerial line was organized under Military control in 1920 between Adana and Aleppo to relieve these two towns while the connecting railroad was in the hands of Turks. Very little mail was carried so that the majority of covers found today are not really flown. None of the cancelling was properly supervised and a great deal was done by favor.

1920

Stamp of France Overprinted.   Perforated
    No watermark.

"*a*"

1 2pi on 15c light green   — — —
2 5pi on 50c blue & red   — — —
    2a. **Piasrtes instead of Piastres.**
3 10pi on 50c lavender & brown   — — —
4 50pi on 1fr greenish olive & claret   — — —

COLUMBIAN REPUBLIC.

The regular 2c carmine stamp of 1917 was surcharged especially for first flight between Barranquilla and Port Colombia, June 18, 1919. Only 210 copies were prepared of which 160 were actually used on covers, leaving only 50 unused copies available.

On account of an experiment by the post office a few stamps appeared without the perforation on one side. These are not defective but were cut in an attempt to facilitate separating the sheets. The attempt was given up as useless almost as soon as undertaken.

We find that there are two types of 1 in the surcharge. The regular Arabic 1 and rarely the Roman I. How many of the latter exist we do not know. There are counterfeits of both, however.

1919 (June 18)   Perforated 14.

    Columbian Issue
       of 1917

    Overprinted.

"a"

1 2c carmine *"a"*   350.00 125.00 200.00

CONGO.

Regular air stamps were issued on July 1st, 1920 for the line Kinshasa — Stanleyville. In September 1922 they were withdrawn and not used again until January 1st, 1928, with the exception of a short time in 1925. After January 31st, 1928 the postal service was extended to Elizabethville, and uniform rates of 1.25fr. for 20 grammes instituted. The original series was reissued in 1928.

1920 (July 1)

No watermark.   Perforated 14.

"*a*"   "*b*"

1	50c	deep orange & black "*a*"	.10	.10	.30
2	1fr	violet & black	.20	.20	.60
3	2fr	blue & black "*b*"	.40	.35	1.20
4	5fr	green & black "*b*"	.85	.85	3.25

COSTA RICA.

In December 1923 there were such heavy rainfalls on the east coast of Costa Rica that the railroads were tied up for weeks, and trade was made to suffer immensely. Arrangements were therefore made with the Republic of Panama, and army planes sent to Costa Rica to fly an air route along the damaged territories. This line however was not an act of the Post Office Department, but was largely responsible for the later line to the Canal Zone, opened in June 1926.

1926 (June 4)   Perforated **12.**

No watermark.

"*a*"

1 20c ultramarine "*a*"   (500,000)   .25   .20   .35

1928   Perforated **12+.**

Lindbergh Issue.

No watermark.

"*b*"

Black Overprint.

2 10c on 12c carmine rose "*b*"   (20,000) 5.00 4.00 5.50

The Lindbergh stamp is a commemorative,
not an airmal stamp. It was issued when
Lindbergh stopped in Costa Rica on his famous
West Indian Flight.

CUBA.

The Pan American Airways, Inc., inaugurated the
daily mail service between Havana and Key West with
their first flight between these points on October 28th,
1927, and have maintained this service up till now. The
first mail had ordinary stamps with a special cancellation,
but before the end of November 1927 the 5c blue air
post stamp of Cuba was in regular use. The service was
started with three Aeromarine flying boats.

On Wednesday morning, February 8th, 1928, Col.
Lindbergh arrived in Havana, Cuba from Port au Prince,
Haiti on the last lap of his Good Will Mission. He
carried three sacks of mail for Havana with him, the first

mail to be carried in the "Spirit of St Louis."The morning
of his arrival the special stamps were issued, 5c red,
same plates as the previous 5c blue, surcharged "Lind-
berg Febrero 1928." .

1927 (Nov. 1)   Perforated 12.

Watermark Star.

"*a*"

1 5c deep blue "*a*"   .15   .10   18

1928
   Lindbergh Issue   **LINDBERGH**   Perforated 12.
   Cuba type of 1927   **FEBRERO 1928**
   Overprinted.
                         "*b*"

2 5c carmine "*b*"   (500,000) .12   .10   .15

CZECHOSLOVAKIA.

The first line was opened on August 15th, 1920 connecting Prague with Paris, London and Warsaw, and regular issues of 1919 imperforate were surcharged. In
January 1921 the same set was issud perforated and
then withdrawn on April 30th. In the spring of 1922
when the air lines were again in operation after a
winter's quiet, and before the new series had come out,
covers were flown with ordinary stamps franked with
a violet cachet, "Letecka Porta-Porte Aerienne." This
occurred between March and June 1st when the new
set came out.

1920 (August 15)
Stamps of
Czechoslovakia
Overprinted in
green, blue
or red.

"*a*"

Imperforate.

No watermark.

1 14kc on 200h ultramarine
   (red) "*a*"   (300,000) 1.20 1.00 1.25
   1a. Overprint inverted.   10.00 — —
   1b. 14kc on 1000h   20.00 — —
2 24kc on 500h reddish brown
   (blue) "*a*"   (300,000) 1.85 1.50 2.25
   2a. Overprint inverted.   10.00 — —
   2b. 24kc on 1000h   20.00 — —
3 28kc on 1000h bright violet
   (green) "*a*"   (300,000) 2.10 1.65 2.75
   3a. Overprint inverted.   10.00 — —
   3b. Double overprint.   20.00 — —
   3c. 28kc on 500h   8.50 — —

1921   Perforated. 14.

4 14kc on 200h ultramarine
   (red) "*a*"   (300,000) 1.20 1.00 1.25
5 24kc on 500h reddish brown
   (blue) "*a*"   (300,000) 1.85 1.50 2.25
6 28kc on 1000h bright violet
   (green) "*a*"   (300,000) 2.10 1.65 2.75
   6a. Overprint inverted.   10.00 — —

1922 (June 14)   Perforated 14.

"*b*"

7 50h on 100h deep green "*b*" (1,620,000)   .06 .05 .08
8 100h on 200h violet "*b*"   (1,730,000)   .12 .10 .15
9 250h on 400h brown "*b*"   (860,000)   .30 .25 .40

DANZIG.

1920

(Sept. 20)   **60**   **60**   MARK **1** MARK   Perforated 14+.

Watermarked
Lozenges.

"a"   *"b"*

1	40pf on 40pf rose red *"a"*	(400,000)	.20	.20	.30
	1a. Double overprint.		—	—	—
2	60pf on 40pf rose red *"a"*	(400,000)	.20	.20	.30
	2.a Double overprint.	(100)	—	—	—
3	1M on 40pf rose red *"b"*	(400,000)	.20	.20	.30

1921 (May 3)

    Watermarked.   Perforated 14+.

    Honeycomb

"c"

4	40pf bluish green *"c"*	.04	.04	.06
	4a. Imperforate.	—	—	—
5	60pf deep violet *"c"*	.04	.04	.08
6	1M carmine *"c"*	.05	.05	.08
7	2M brownish orange *"c"*	.06	.06	.10
	7a. Watermark large horizontal honeycomb.	—	—	—

     Rouletted 13+   

"d"

8	5M bluish violet *"d"*		.08	.08	.12
	8a. Imperforate.	(200)	10.00	—	—
9	10M dark green *"d"*		.20	.20	.35
	9a. Watermark large horizontal honeycomb.		—	—	—

1923 (Jan. 2)

    Watermarked   Perforated 14+.
      Webbing.

10	40pf bluish green *"c"*	.03	.02	.05
11	60pf deep violet *"c"*	.03	.02	.05
12	1M carmine *"c"*	.03	.02	.05
13	2M brownish orange *"c"*	.03	.02	.05

      Rouletted 13+

14	5M bluish violet *"d"*	.05	.04	.10
15	10M dark green *"d"*	.06	.05	.12

    Paper with Gray
      Network.

16	20M brownish orange *"d"*		.08	.08	.10
	16a. Without network.	(400)	—	—	—

                            Perforated 14, 14+.

17	24M light blue *"c"*		.02	.02	.03
18	50M bright orange *"d"*		.04	.03	.06
	18a. Without network.	(200)	—	—	—
19	100M red *"d"*		.04	.03	.06
20	250M brown *"d"*		.05	.04	.10
	20a. Without network.	(50)	—	—	—
21	500M rose carmine *"d"*		.08	.08	.15

1923 (Oct. 18)   Perforated 14, 14+.

             "e"

22	250,000M bright red *"e"*		.03	.02	.05
	22a. Watermarked vertical hexagons.	(100)	30.00	—	—
	22b. Imperforate	(400)	10.00	—	—

                            Imperforate.

23	500,000M bright red *"e"*		.03	.02	.05
	23a. Watermarked vertical hexagons.	(400)	8.00	—	—
	23b. Imperforate	(400)	10.00	—	—

Overprinted.

2

Millionen

"*f*"

24 2mil on 100,000M bright red .03 .02 .05
   24a. Watermarked vertical hexagons. (300) 10.00 — —
   24b. Without overprint. (100) 30.00 — —
25 5mil on 50,000M bright red .03 .02 .05
   25a. 5mil. on 10,000. 3.00 3.00 5.00
   25b. Watermarked vertical hexagons. (200) 15.00 — —

1924 (May 1) Perforated 14.

"*g*"   "*h*"

26 10pf vermilion "*g*" .07 .05 .10
27 20pf carmine "*g*" .14 .05 .10
28 40pf brownish olive "*g*" .28 .20 .35
29 1g green "*g*" .60 .50 .72
30 2½g brownish violet "*h*" 1.50 1.20 1.75

DENMARK.

Several varieties of quite interesting private and se-mi-official stamps have been printed in Denmark, but the only official issue, a series of three stamps, came out 1925-26 for the regular Trans-European lines.

1925-26

Watermarked Crosses.

"*a*"

Perforated 11, 12.

1	10ö yellowish green "*a*"		.10	.08	.15
2	15ö violet "*a*"		.12	.10	.20
3	25ö bright red "*a*"		.20	.18	.30

=====

DOMINICAN REPUBLIC.

The Dominican Republic issued its first airmail stamps in 1928, for use on lines between Cuba, Jamaica, Haiti and San Domingo.

1928

No watermark.

"*a*"

Perforated 11÷.

1	10c ultramarine "*a*"	.25	.25	.35

DUTCH INDIES.

1928
Overprinted.

LUCHTPOST
10

LUCHTPOST

40 40

LUCHTPOST

75 Ct

"a"   "b"   "c"

1	10 on 12½c scarlet "a"	.15	.10	.20
2	20 on 25c mauve "a"	.30	.20	.40
3	40 on 80c orange "b"	.60	.50	.90
4	75c on 1g sepia (B) "c"	.95	.80	1.25
5	1½ on 2½g carmine rose "c"	1.80	1.50	2.50

EGYPT.

The first flight organized in Egypt was in February 1914 between Heliopolis — Khartoum. Only a few covers were carried franked with ordinary stamps of Egypt or Sudan, and then cancelled with a special violet cachet. In December 1918, a Cairo to Delhi, India flight was planned by the British airforce authorities, but the Handly Page machine was forced to land at Calcuta, and the thirty covers carried were forwarded in the usual way. The railroad strike in March-April 1919 caused the inauguration of an aerial line between Port Said — Alexandria — Cairo. Various cachets were used on this line with ordinary stamps of Egypt. In 1923 a regular line was opened between Cairo and Bagdad via Jerusalem and letters received special cachets. The first air stamp of Egypt was not issued however, until 1926. It was used on the regular Cairo-Bagdad service.

1926 (March 10)
Watermarked.
Multiple Crown.

Perforated 13+.

"a"

1 27M dark violet *"a"*   .45   .45   .60

ESTHONIA.

The first mail flight was made by military machines
on Feb. 7th, 1920 between Reval and Helsingfors, but
the special airmail stamp did not come out until Feb.
28th, 1920. The second line between Tallinn — Helsingfors was opened on October 1st, 1923, and the first stamp
was printed for this occasion. Lines were also opened
to Riga and Konigsberg.

1920 (Feb. 28)
No watermark.

Imperforate.

"a"

1 5M blue, black & yellow *"a"* (511,643) .20   .15   .25

1923 (Oct. 1)
Esthonian Issue of 1920
Overprinted "1923"
in vermilion.

"b"

No watermark.

2 5M blue, black & yellow *"b"* (45,800) .30   .30   .40

Pairs of Esthonian 1920 Stamps
Overprinted in black or vermilion.

10 Marka

1923

"c"   "d"

3	10M on 5M+5M blue, black & yellow "d"	(40,300)	.55	.50	.65
4	15M on 5M blue, black & yellow "c"	(45,400)	.55	.50	.65
5	20M on 5M+5M blue, black & yellow "d"	(30,200)	1.00	1.00	1.25
6	45M on 5M+5M blue, black & yellow "d"	(13,124)	3.25	3.25	4.00

Perforated 11+.

7	10M on 5M+5M blue, black & yellow	(300)	8.00	—	—
8	20M on 5M+5M blue, black & yellow	(2,000)	2,50	—	—

1924 (Feb. 16)   Imperforate.

"e"

9	5M black & yellow "e"	(52,448)	.10	.10	.15
10	10M black & blue "e"	(52,248)	.15	.15	20
11	15M black & red "e"	(52,340)	.30	.30	.40
12	20M black & green "e"	(51,268)	.40	.40	.60
13	45M black & violet "e"	(36,800)	.80	.80	1.25

1925 (May 3)   Perforated 13+.

14	5M black & yellow "e"	(53,222)	.06	.05	.10
15	10M black & blue "e"	(53,122)	.08	.06	.12
16	15M black & red "e"	(52,572)	.12	.10	.18
17	20M black & green "e"	(52,322)	.18	.15	.25
18	45M black & violet "e"	(29,123)	.40	30	.50

FRANCE.

A regular air line was started March 1st, 1919 between Paris — Bordeaux — Marseilles, but no special stamps or cachets were used.

France's air stamps were issued on the occasion of the 1st International Exposition of Aviation and Navigation held at Marseilles from June 15th, to July 15th, 1927. About 60,000 pairs were sold and the balance officially destroyed.

Covers bearing these stamps are only from the flight Marseilles — Algiers with hexagon cancellation.

1928

Ille de France
Overprints.

The experimental "Ship to Shore" flight from the steamship Ile de France produced an issue of stamps novel in conception and of great historical interest. The idea of the ship to shore service was to expedite the delivery of trans-Atlantic mail in the country of destination. On the Ile de France's trip from Havre to New York the experimental flight, August 13th, 1928, was so largely patronized as to exhaust the supply of French stamps of appropriate denomination available aboard ship. The rate for ordinary letters was 10 Francs 50 Centimes and for registered letters 13 Francs 50 Centimes.

It was desired to repeat the experiment on August 23rd during the return trip to France. In order to provide the necessary stamps, the French Consul General at New York, M. Maxine Mangendre, authorized the following overprinting:

1,000 copies — 1 Franc 50 Centimes — blue "Pasteur".
3,000 copies — 90 Centimes — dull red Beuthelot".

All were surcharged 10 Francs in black ink in panes of 50

One sheet of the 10 Franc on 90c dull red is brown with inverted overprint.

1927 (June 25)
    Overprinted in
Deep blue or black on
    French Stamps.

Poste Aérienne
"*a*"

    Perforated 13+, 14.
    No Watermark

1 2fr orange & blue (blue) "*a*" (60,000) 1.50 1.50 3.00
2 5fr dark blue & buff (black)"*a*"(60,000) 1.50 1.50 3.00

1928 (August 20)

    Ille de France Issue.   Perforated 13+, 14.

"*b*"   "*c*"

3 10fr on 90c dull red "*b*"   (3,000) 30.00 25.00 30.00
4 10fr on 1.50fr blue "*c*"   (1,000) 90.00 80.00 90.00

GERMANY.

    Germany has an immense amount of semi-official stamps and flights, as well as innumerable first and special flights and cancellation varieties which only a few most specialized collectors are really interested in. As early as 1893 balloon flights are recorded; and almost every year after that from one to a dozen noteworthy flights occurred. In August 1911, the aviator Hoffman, carried the first mail in Germany by airplane from Berlin to Frankfurt. The mail consisted of a bag of the

"Berlin Morning Post." This was the fourth airplane flight in the history of airmail.

Important landmarks in the development of aerial transportation such as the flight of the "ZR-3" across the Atlantic and the flight of the "Graf Zeppelin" LZ-127 in October 1928, are listed in the section, "Historical Flights."

1919

No watermark.   Perforated 14+, 15.

"a"   "b"

1	10pf orange "a"	.02	.02	.04
2	40pf deep green "b"	.02	.02	.04

1922-23

Watermarked.

"c"

3	25pf chocolate brown "c"	.10	.10	.15
4	40pf orange "c"	.08	.08	.10
5	50pf violet "c"	.02	.02	.03
6	60pf carmine "c"	.07	.06	.08
7	80pf bluish green "c"	.07	.06	.08
8	1M light green & deep green "c"	.02	.02	.03
9	2M gray & lake "c"	.02	.02	.03
10	3M gray & blue "c"	.02	.02	.03
11	5M yellow & reddish orange "c"	.02	.02	.03
12	10M rose & violet "c"	.02	.02	.03

13 25M yellow & brown *"c"*   .02   .02   .03
14 100M rose & greenish olive *"c"*   .05   .05   .10

1923

15   5M vermilion *"c"*   .02   .02   .03
16   10M deep violet *"c"*   .02   .02   .03
17   25M deep brown *"c"*   .02   .02   .03
18 100M greenish olive *"c"*   .02   .02   .03
19 200M dark blue *"c"*   .02   .02   .03
    19a. Imperforate   8.00   —   —

1924

20   5pf light green *"c"*   (7,500,000)   .05   .03   .10
21   10pf carmine *"c"*   (7,500,000)   .10   .06   .16
22   20pf blue violet *"c"*   (7,500,000)   .20   .15   .25
23   50pf orange *"c"*   (7,500,000)   .50   .40   .60
24 100pf violet *"c"*   (7,200,000)   1.00   .75 1.25
25 200pf greenish blue *"c"*   (6,370,000)   2.00 1.25 2.25
26 300pf pale gray *"c"*   (6,350,000)   3.00 2.25 3.50

1926

"d"

27   5pf green *"d"*   .04   .02   .05
28   10pf reddish rose *"d"*   .0.6 .03   .08
29   20pf dark blue *"d"*   .12   .08   .15
30   50pf brown orange *"d"*   .30   .20   .40
31   1M pale red & black *"d"*   .60   .40   .70
32   2M blue & black *"d"*   1.20   .80 1.40
33   3M greenish olive & black *"d"*   1.80 1.50 2.00

1927

34 15pf lilac rose *"d"*   .10   .04   .06

1928

"Graf Zeppelin" Issue.

Watermarked.

Perforated 14.

"*e*"

35 2M ultramarine "*e*"   1.25 1.50 2.00
36 4M black brown "*e*"   2.50 2.75 3.50

GREECE.

The curious set of Greek airmails was issued November 3rd, 1926 for the line Brindisi — Athens — Constantinople and the inscription reads: "Aerial Postal communication Italy — Greece — Turkey." The stamps are used for collection of revenue for the company running the line, 2d for postals, 3d for newspapers, 5d for letters and 10d for registered letters. Regular Italian, Greek or Turkish stamps must be used as well. It is understood that due to a change in regulation, these stamps are now sold by the government. We have listed them on the strength of this information.

1926

Chalky Paper.

No watermark.

Perforated 11+

"*a*"

1 2d black, blue, yellow, violet
        & rose   (100,000) .10 .08 .15
2 3d black, rose, green, violet,

3	5d black, rose, violet, light brown & blue	(100,000)	.15 .12 .20
4	10d black, green, yellow, lilac, blue & rose	(100,000)	.50 .40 .55

HONDURAS.

The first series of stamps were issue in May, 1925 for the service, Tequayalpa to San Pedro Sula and to Puerto Cortez. This service only lasted about two months and carried very few letters.

Counterfeits exist of all Honduras air stamps, some even bearing the guarantee of supposedly reliable people.

1925

Honduras Stamp of 1915
Overprinted in
blue, red and black.

**AERO
CORREO**

"a"

Perforated 11+.

No watermark.

1	5c pale blue (black) "a"	(500)	25.00	20.00	—
	1a. "AFRO"		—	—	—
2	5c pale blue (blue) "a"	(200)	35.00	30.00	—
	2a. Vertical overprint.	(12)	—	—	—
	2b. Inverted overprint.		—	—	—
3	5c pale blue (red) "a"	(5)	850.00	—	—
4	10c deep blue (red) "a"	(500)	25.00	20.00	—
	4a. Inverted overprint.		—	—	—
	4b. Tete beche.		—	—	—
5	10c deep blue (black) "a"	(48)	350.00	350.00	—
6	20c brown (black) "a"	(500)	25.00	20.00	—
	6a. Inverted overprint.		—	—	—
	6b. Tete beche.		—	—	—
	6c. "AFRO".		—	—	—
	6d. Double overprint.		—	—	—
7	20c brown (blue) "a"	(200)	35.00	30.00	—
	7a. Inverted overprint.	(24)	—	—	—
	7b. Tete beche.		—	—	—
	7c. Vertical overprint.		—	—	—
8	50c dull red (black) "a"	(200)	55.00	50.00	—
	8a. Inverted overprint.	(36)	—	—	—
9	1p light yellow geen (black) "a"	(100)	100,00	90.00	—

Overprinted.   **AERO**

No watermark.   **CORREO**
                            ■   **25**   ■

                                "b"

10 20c on 1c dark chocolate
        (black) *"b"*   (500)   25.00   20.00   —
    10a. Inverted overprint.   —   —   —
11 25c on 5c pale blue
        (blue) *"b"*   (300)   30.00   25.00   —
    11a. Inverted overprint.   —   --   —
12 25c on 20c brown (blue) *"b"* (300) 30.00   25.00   —
    12a. Tete beche.   —   —   —
    12b. Inverted overprint.   —   —   —

=====

HUNGARY.

A line connecting Budapest and Vienna was opened
in the summer of 1918 using military planes. Unfortunately, two serious accidents terminated the service
which lasted only 19 days, July 4th to July 23rd. Flown
covers of this period are rare. They are cancelled either
with ordinary or special cachets.

The next line was not opened until November 2nd,
1920 between Budapest — Szombathely and Budapest—
Szeged and continued through the winter until April 9th,
1921 when it was terminated by order of the Allied
Powers. It is very interesting to note that on this line
mail was carried for towns where the planes did not land
but dropped the bags by means of parachutes. Covers
addressed to Gyor, Papa, Nagy-Kosos and Kiskunfele-
ghaza were dropped in this manner.

1918 (March 6)

Regular Hungarian
　Stamps of 1916
　Overprinted.

Watermarked.
Double Cross.

Perforated 14+.

"a"

1　1k 50f on 75f bright blue (red) *"a"*		.30	.25	.50
1a. Inverted overprint.	(100)	35.00	—	—
2　4k 50f on 2k dull brown (blue) *"a"*		.55	.45	.85

1920 (Nov. 7)

Same, with different
　Overprint under
　Republic.

"b"

3　3k on 10k brown & bright violet (green) *"b"*	.03	.03	.08
4　8k on 10k brown & bright violet (red) *"b"*	.05	.05	.10
5　12k on 10k brown & bright violet (blue) *"b"*	.06	.05	.15

1924 (April 11)

Watermarked.
Double Cross.

Perforated 14.

"c"　　　　　　　*"d"*

6　100k reddish brown & red *"c"*	.05	.03	.10
7　500k bluish green & light green *"c"*	.07	.05	.15

8	1000k light brown & brown "c"	.12	.10	.20
9	2000k deep blue & pale blue "c"	.20	.18	.30
10	5000k dark violet & violet "d"	.40	.30	.60
11	10000k red & dark violet "d"	.80	.60	1.20

1927 (Sept. 1)

Watermarked.
Four Double Crosses.   Perforated 14.

"e"   "f"

12	12f dark green "e"	.06	.05	.10
13	16f reddish brown "e"	.10	.06	.12
14	20f bright red "e"	.12	.08	.15
15	32f violet brown "e"	.20	.15	.25
16	40f dark ultramarine "e"	.22	.18	.30
17	50f claret red "f"	.25	.20	.35
18	72f greenish olive "f"	.40	.30	.50
19	80f dark violet "f"	.45	.35	.65

ICELAND.

Iceland's initiation into aviation came October 17th, 1919 when Capt. Cecil Farber, late R. A. F., established a commercial aviation company, and showed the island its first airplane.

The air stamp of June, 1928, was issued for the new mail line from Reykjebik to Stockholm, Sweden.

1928   Perforated 14, 14+
Regular Issue of Iceland
          1920
Overprinted Airplane.

"*a*"

Watermarked Multiple Crosses.
1 10 öre dull carmine "*a*"   .12   .12   .15

ITALY.

The first experimental flights were made in May
1917 by the Italian government, between Turin—Rome
and between Naples—Palermo, but no regular lines were
instituted although the experimental flights were most
successful. In connection with these flights, Italy issued
two air stamps, special deliveries, surcharged, and not
more than ten copies were sold to an individual to prevent speculation. This makes Italy the first country
to issue an official airmail stamp.

On March 2nd, 1919 a line was opened between
Padna and Vienna, a distance of 304 miles. No special
stamps or cancellations were employed.

On April 1st, 1926, at the opening of the line Turin-
Trieste, a set of four stamps was issued.

1917 (May 22)
     Italian Special Delivery Stamp   Perforated 14.
          of 1903 overprinted.
     Watermarked Crowns.

     "*a*"   "*b*"

1 25c rose red "*a*"   (200,000)   .40   .50 1.00
2 25c on 40c bright violet "*b*" (130,000)   .50   .45   .65

1926-28

Watermarked Crowns.

"c"   "d"

3 50c rose "c"	.08	.06	.10
4 50c on 60c light gray "d"	.12	.10	.22
5 60c light gray "c"	.10	.06	.15
6 80c on I L dull blue "d"	.20	.15	.35
7 1L blue "c"	.16	.12	.25
8 1.20L brown "c"	.20	.15	.22
9 1.50L light brown "c"	.25	.20	.35
10 5L dull green "c"	.75	.65	1.00

JAPAN.

An American pilot by the name of Atwater, was the first to carry air mail in Japan. In June 1912 he flew between Tokyo and Yokahoma with a Curtiss Hydroplane carrying about 1,000 post cards cancelled with a special souvenir cachet. Regular postage stamps were used, however, and the flight was regarded as a pure experiment.

Regular aerial service was started on October 3rd, 1919 between Tokyo and Osaka, and the 1½ and 3 sen stamps were surcharged with an aeroplane for the service. Bad weather however, prevented the planes from taking off, and all mail went by rail the next day, October 4th. The only flights actually completed were on October 22nd and 23rd between Tokyo-Osaka and return. These covers bear cachets dated October 20th, the date planned for the flights. Stamps were recalled at the end of 1919.

In the fall of 1919, the Japanese government appropriated $125,000,000 to be spent in the development of the air services. However up to the present no great improvements have been made as far as the aerial mail service is concerned all the money being devoted apparently to military aviation.

1919 (Oct. 3)   Perforated 11, 13+.
Japanese stamps of 1914

    Overprinted in
    blue or red.

"*a*"

    Watermarked Wavy Lines.
        Granite Paper.

1 1½ sen blue (red) "*a*"   2.50 3.25 10.00
2 3   sen bright rose (blue) "*a*"   3.50 4.00 15.00

LATVIA.

A line was opened between Riga and Revel on July 31st, 1921 and extended to Memel and Königsberg a little later. The triangular air stamps issued for this occasion were intended to be perforated, but on account of some damage to the perforating machine, they had to be sold imperforate for the fiirst week or so of the lines' existance.

A second series of stamps was issued May 1st, 1928 for the line Berlin — Koenigsberg — Moscow — Leningrad, which stopped at Riga.

1921 (July 31)

Watermarked Vertical
    Wavy Lines.

"*a*"

Perforated 11+.

1 10r bright green "*a*"	(185,000)	.20	.20	.25
1a. Pair, imperforate between.				
2 20r blue "*a*"	(85,000)	.40	.40	.50
2a. Pair, imperforate between.				

Imperforate.

3 10r bright green "*a*"	(15,000)	1.00	1.00	1.25
4 20r dark blue "*a*"	(15,000)	1.00	1.00	1.25

1928

Watermarked Wavy Lines.   Perforated 11.

5 10s dark green "*a*"	.80	.05	.10
6 15s deep red "*a*"	.12	.10	.15
7 25s ultramarine "*a*"	.20	.15	.22

LEBANON.

First series of air stamps came out in January 1924
for the line: Beyrout — Latakia — Bagdad. The surcharge was made at the printing house of the Capuchin
Fathers in Beyrout, and shows many minor varieties
which need not be listed.

1924 (Jan. 21)   **Poste par Avion**   Perforated 12+, 13+.
  French Issue of 1924   **GRAND LIBAN**
    Overprinted.
  No watermark.   **5 PIASTRES**

"*a*"

1	2pi on 40c red & light blue "*a*"	(15,750)	.80	.60	1.00
2	3pi on 60c violet & ultramarine "*a*"	(15,750)	.80	.60	1.00
3	5pi on 1fr claret & olive bistre "*a*"	(15,750)	.80	.60	1.00
4	10pi on 2fr orange & light blue "*a*"	(15,750)	.80	.60	1.00

4a.   Inverted overprint.   —   —   —

1924 (July 10)

French Issue of 1924 Overprinted.

Gᵈ Liban 2 Piastres
جبل لبنان الكبير
غروش ٢

Avion

"*b*"

5	2pi on 40c red & light blue "*b*"	(45,000)	.35	.30	.60
6	3pi on 60c violet & ultramarine "*b*"	(44,700)	.35	.30	.60
7	5pi on 1fr claret & olive bistre "*b*"	(51,000)	.35	.30	.60
8	10pi on 2fr orange & light blue "*b*"	(47,750)	.35	.30	.60

1925 (March 1)
Lebanon, Regular Issue of 1925
Overprnted in green.

AVION
طيّارة

"*c*"

9	2pi brown "*c*"	.25	.20	.35
10	3pi brownish orange "*c*"	.25	.20	.35
11	5pi violet "*c*"	.25	.20	.35
12	10pi brownish violet "*c*"	.35	.25	.35

1926
Lebanon, Regular Issue of 1925
Overprinted in red.

"*d*"

13 2pi brown *"d"*	.25	.20	.30
14 3pi brownish orange *"d"*	.25	.20	.30
15 5pi violet *"d"*	.25	.20	.30
16 10pi brownish violet *"d"*	.35	.25	.30

1927

Lebanon, Regular Issue of 1925
Overprinted.

17 2pi brown	.25	.20	.35
18 3pi brownish orange	.25	.20	.35
19 5pi violet	.30	.25	.45
20 10pi brownish violet	.45	.40	.55

1928

Lebanon, Regular Issue of 1927
With additional overprint in black.

21 2pi brown	.35	.30	.50
22 3pi brownish orange	.35	.30	.50
23 5pi violet	.35	.30	.50
24 10pi brownish violet	.50	.40	.75

Same Overprint in red.

25 2pi brown	.10	.08	.15
26 3pi brownish orange	.14	.10	.20
27 5pi violet	.25	.20	.30
28 10pi brownish violet	.45	.40	.50
29 2pi brown	.10	.08	.15
30 3pi brownish orange	.14	.10	.20
31 5pi violet	.25	.20	.30
32 10pi brownish violet	.45	.40	.50

LITHUANIA.

1921

Watermarked Webbing.   Perforated 11+.

"a"

"b"

"c"

"d"

1	20sk ultramarine "a"	(201,645)	.10	.12	.15
2	40sk orange red "a"	(201,600)	.10	.12	.15
3	60sk green "a"	(201,600)	.12	.15	.15
4	80sk rose "a"	(201,600)	.15	.20	.20
	4a. Horizontal pair Imperforate between (100)		10.00	—	—
5	1auk red & green "b"	(200,000)	.35	.45	.45
	5a. Imperforate.	(4,378)	2.00	—	—
6	2auk blue & brown "c"	(203,325)	.55	.65	.65
7	5auk dull blue & yellow "d"	(204,600)	.65	.75	.75

1921 (Nov. 6)   Perforated 11+.

Watermarked Webbing.

"e"

8	20sk blue & orange "c"	(100,000)	.10	.10	.20

9	60sk lake & dark blue "c"	(100,000)	.10	.10	.20
10	60sk green&bluish violet "c"	(100,000)	.10	.10	.20
11	80sk dark green & buff "c"	(100,000)	.10	.10	.20
12	1auk blue & green "e"	(100,000)	.12	.12	.25
13	2auk orange brown & gray "e"	(100,000)	.15	.15	.30
14	5auk metallic blue&lilac "e"	(100,000)	.15	.15	.30

This set (8-14) was issued to Commemorate the opening of the Air Post Service.

1922 (July 15)

Watermarked Webbing.   Perforated 11, 11+.

"f"

15	1auk red & brown olive "f"	(106,703)	.15	.15	.25
16	3auk green & violet "f"	(107,135)	.25	.25	.35
	16a. Imperforate at bottom.		—	—	—
17	5auk yellow & dark blue "f"	(120,635)	.35	.35	.45
	17a. Yellow arc under ""Auks."		1.00	—	—

1922 (July 22)

Watermarked Webbing.

Perforated 11, 11+.

"g"

18	2auk rose & blue "g"	(203,000)	.10	.10	.15
19	4auk rose & brown "g"	(200,000)	.15	.15	.25
20	10auk dull blue & black "g"	(203,000)	.20	.20	.30

1922 (Oct. 10)

Overprinted new Values
in black or red.   Perforated 11, 11+.

Watermarked webbing.

21 10c on 20 sk ultramarine "*a*" (21,580)   .50   .50   .70
    21a. Watermark vertical.   2.00 2.00   —
22 10c on 40sk orane red "*a*"   (21,600)   .50   .50   .70
23 10c on 60sk green "*a*"   (21,600)   .50   .50   .70
    23a. Watermark vertical.   —   —   —
24 10c on 80sk rose "*a*"   (21,600)   .50   .50   .70
25 20c on 1auk red & green "*b*"   (12,100) 2.25 2.00 3.50
26 20c on 2 auk blue &
    brown "*c*"   (9.880) 3.25 3.00 4.25
    26a. Without "Cent"   —   —   —
27 25c on 2auk blue & rose "*g*"   (87,200)   .35   .30   .50
    27a. Inverted overprint.   8.00 7.50 10.00
28 30c on 4auk rose & brown "*g*" (93,800)   .25   .20   .35
29 50c on 5auk dull blue &
    yellow "*d*"   (77,180)   .40   .35   .60
30 50c on10auk blue & black "*g*" (102,400)   .45   .45   .70
    30a. Inverted overprint.   5.00 4.50 6.50
31 1 litas on 5auk yellow & dull
    blue "*f*"   (10,150) 3.25 3.00 4.50
    31a. Yellow arc under "Auks"   10.00   —   —

1924 (Jan. 28)

Watermarked Parquetry.   Perforated **11.**

          "*h*"   "*i*"

32 20c yellow "*h*"   (953,650)   .12   .10   .20
33 40c bright green "*h*"   (353,200)   .25   .25   .35
    33a. Horizontal pair, imperf. between.   7.50   —   —
    33b. Vertical pair, imperf. between.   7.50   —   —
34 60c rose "*h*"   (554,600)   .35   .35   .50
35 1 Litas brown "*i*"   (951,800)   .55   .55   .75

1924

Same, No watermark.

36	20c yellow "h"	(200)	35.00 — —
37	60c rose red "h"	(200)	27.50 35.00 —

1924 (March 2)

Same Overprinted for benefit of
Red Cross

No watermark.

38	20c+20c yellow "h"	(50,500)	.35	.35	.50
39	40c+40c bright green "h"	(50,500)	.55	.55	.75
40	60c+60c rose "h"	(50,500)	.80	.80	1.00
41	1L+1L brown "i"	(50,500)	1.50	1.50	2.00

Same No watermark.

42	60c+60c rose "h"	(200)	45.00 — —

1926 (June 17)

Watermarked Intersecting
Diamonds.

"k"

Perforated 14+.

43	20c rose carmine "k"	(500,000)	.08	.04	.12
	43a. Horizontal pair, imperforate between.		7.50	—	—
	43b. Vertical pair, imperforate between.		7.50	—	—
44	40c orange & violet "k"	(500,000)	.16	.08	.20
	44a. Horizontal pair, imperforate between.		8.50	—	—
	44b. Vertical pair, imperforate between.		8,50	—	—
45	60c black & blue "k"	(500,000)	.25	.20	.35
	45a Horizontal pair, imperforate between.		9.50	—	—
	45b. Vertical pair, imperf. between.		9.50	—	—
	45c. Center Inverted.		25.00	—	—

MALTA.

Malta issued its first air stamps quite unexpectedly on April 1st, 1928, in the form of a current six penny stamp surcharged "Air Mail," to be used on the weekly mail service for Iraq, Egypt and Persia which is maintained by the Postal Administration of the United Kingdom. Following are extracts from Government notices:

"It is hereby notified that as from the 1st April next, Air Mails will be made up at this Office for Iraq, Persia, North-East Arabia, and North-West India by the Egypt, Egypt-Iraq Mail Service, maintained by the Postal Administration of the United Kingtom. Such mails will be despatched to Gaza, Baghdad, Basra, via Egypt in alternate weeks as follows:

Week commencing 2nd April:
Monday at 8 p. m.

Week commencing 9th April:
Thursday at 8 p. m.

The gain in time in respect of mails for Baghdad will be of 16 days; that in respect of mails for Basra of 13, and that in respect of mails for Karachi of 2 days — the latter beeing carried by sea from Basra. The provinces in India served with advantage by this Service will be Baluchistan, Kashmir, N. W. Frontier, Punjab, Sind.

GENERAL POST OFFICE,

20th March, 1928."

"With reference to paragraph 3 (b) of the Notice issued by the Postmaster-General on the 20th instant, regarding Air Mails, it is hereby notified that the payment of the Air Mail Fee of 6d., therein referred to will be denoted by means of special stamp only. For this purpose, stamps at 6d. in current use, printed on white paper, King's Head, violet on red ground, and overprinted with the words "Air Mail," will be on sale at the Post Office as in Malta and Gozo as from the 1st April, 1928.

March 28th, 1928.

STRICKLA,
Minister for Posts."

1928

Malta Regular Issue
Overprinted.

Watermarked
Multiple Crown &
Script C. A.

"a"

Perforated 14.

1   6d crimson red & violet *"a"*   .25 .25   .35

MEMEL.

1921 (July)

Memel Regular Issue of
1920-21 Overprinted
in dark blue.
Unwatermarked.

"a"

Perforated 14, 13+.

		4 A	**4** B	
1 60pf on 40c light blue & red (15,500)		8.00	8.00	10.00
1a. colored dot in center of T. (2,500)		12.00	12.00	15.00
2 80pf on 45c blue & green (100,000)		.35	.35	.50
3 1M on 50c lavender & pale brown (150,000)		.25	.25	.35
4 2M on 1fr greenish olive & claret (100,000)		.35	.35	.50
4a. "Flugpost" inverted. (75)		80.00	—	—
5 4M on 2fr light blue & orange (Type A) (60,000)		.85	.85	1.00
5a. Type B. (1,200)		25.00	—	—

New Value with Initial
Capital.

6 60pf on 40c light blue & red (80,000)		.75	.75	1.00
6a. "Flugpost" inverted. (75)		80.00	—	—
7 3M on 60c ultramarine & violet (100,000)		.45	.35	.65
7a. "Flugpost" inverted. (75)		80.00	—	—

1922 (May 12)

Memel regular issue of
1922 Overprinted.

Unwatermarked.

"b"

8 40pf on 40c red & light blue (120,000)		.20	.15	.25
9 80pf on 45c blue & green (120,000)		.20	.15	.25

10	1M on 40c light blue & red	(120,000)	.20	.15	.25
11	1.25M on 60c ultramarine & violet	(120,000)	.20	.15	.25
12	1.50M on 45c blue & green	(120,000)	.20	.15	.25
13	2M on 1fr greenish olive & claret	(120,000)	.20	.15	.25
14	3M on 60c ultramarine & violet	(120,000)	.20	.15	.25
15	5M on 1fr greenish olive & claret	(120,000)	.20	.15	.25
16	6M on 2fr light blue & orange	(120,000)	.20	.15	.25
17	9M on 5fr light brown & blue	(120,000)	.20	.15	.25

Same Overprinted on Regular Issue
of 1920-21.

18	3M on 60c ultramarine & violet	(4,000)	7.50	7.50	10.00
19	4M on 2fr light blue & orange	(120,000)	.20	.15	.25

1922 (Oct. 18)
Memel Regular Issue   **FLUGPOST**
of 1922 Overprinted
in black or red.

"*c*"

20	40pf on 40c light blue & red	(100,000)	.10	.10	.15
21	1M on 40c light blue & red	(100,000)	.10	.10	.15
22	1.25M on 60c ultramarine & violet (red)	(100,000)	.10	.10	.15
23	1.50M on 45c blue & green (red)	(100,000)	.10	.10	.15
24	2M on 1fr greenish olive & claret	(100,000)	.10	.10	.15
25	3M on 60c ultramarine & violet (red)	(100,000)	.10	.10	.15
26	4M on 2fr light blue & orange	(100,000)	.10	.10	.15
27	5M on 1fr greenish olive & claret	(100,000)	.10	.10	.15
28	6M on 2fr light blue & orange	(100,000)	.10	.10	.15
29	9M on 5fr light brown & blue (red)	(100,000)	.10	.10	.15

MEXICO.

Only one air line was atempted by the postal authorities, and this ended disastrously.

On April 15th, 1922 a line was started between Mexico City — Guadalajara — Tepic. On account of hurricanes, accidents and general adverse conditions the mail did not arrive in Tepic until April 18th, a much longer time than the ordinary route. Upon this the stamp was withdrawn.

In 1927 the same type of stamp was printed with watermark and used for special delivery parcel post, pending the opening of an aerial line.

On April 15th, 1928 a line was inaugurated between Tampico and Mexico City via Tuxpan, and a new 25c stamp of same design as the previous 50c was used. Sale of the 50c stamp was stopped on April 1st. Approximately 2,000 letters were carried either way on the first flights of April 15th, with the new 25c stamp.

"*a*"

1922 (April 2)			Perforated 12.
No watermark.			

1 50c reddish brown & blue "*a*"   5.00 7.50 8.50

1927 (October 13)

Watermarked CORREOS MEXICO.   Perforated 12.

2 50c reddish brown & deep blue "*a*"   1.75 1.75 2.50
2a. Imperforate between (10)   —   —   —

1928

Watermarked CORREOS MEXICO.   Perforated **12.**

3 25c carmine brown & brown *"a"*   .80   .60 1.00

1928

Type of 1922 Issue.   Perforated **12.**
Watermarked CORREOS MEXICO.

4 25c grayish brown & green *"a"*   .25   .30   .35

MOROCCO.

An aerial line was established between Casablanca and Toulouse by the French company "Societe Latecoere," and the first regular air stamps were used on January 2nd, 1922.

1922   Perforated **13+**
No watermark.

"a"

1 75c dark blue *"a"*		8.00	4.00	10.00
2 1fr vermilion *"a"*		.75	.55	1.20
3 2fr violet *"a"*		2.00	1.50	2.50
3a. Imperforated	(50)	—	—	—

1922-23

4 25c ultramarine *"a"*		.75	.55	1.20
4a. Imperforated.	(50)			
5 50c blue green *"a"*		.40	.30	.60
5a. Imperforated.	(100)	—	—	—
6 75c dark green *"a"*		.35	.25	.55
6a. Imperforated.	(50)	—	—	—

1927

7	5c orange *"a"*		.12	.10	.15
8	80c brownish violet *"a"*		.10	.10	.15
9	1.40fr lake *"a"*		.25	.20	.35
10	1.90fr dark blue *"a"*		.35	.30	.40
11	2fr dark violet *"a"*		.45	.40	.60
12	3fr black *"a"*		.50	.45	.60

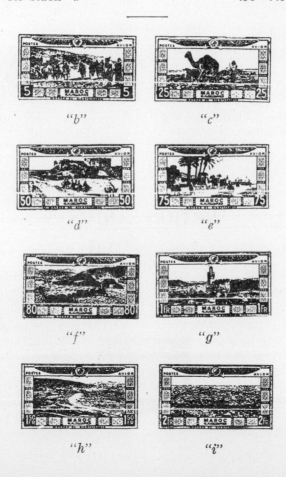

"b"   *"c"*

"d"   *"e"*

"f"   *"g"*

"h"   *"i"*

"j"　　　　　　　　"k"

1928

No watermark.　　　　　　　　　Perforated 13, 14.

13	5c dark blue "b"	.05	.05	.06
14	25c brownish orange "c"	.10	.10	.12
15	50c red "d"	.15	.15	.18
16	75c brownish orange "e"	.20	.20	.22
17	80c greenish olive "f"	.25	.25	.30
18	1fr orange "g"	.35	.35	.40
19	1.50fr metalic blue "h'"	.40	.40	.45
20	2fr brown "i"	.50	.50	.60
21	3fr dark violet "j"	1.00	1.00	1.20
22	5fr black brown "k"	1.50	1.50	1.65

NETHERLANDS.

The air stamps issued May 1st, 1921 were used in addition to the regular postage on all international lines that touched at Amsterdam. They were withdrawn June 1st, 1922,, but later placed on sale again, and even used for ordinary postage.

1921 (May 1)　　　　　　　　　　Perforated 12, 13.
No watermark.

"a"

1 10c red "a"　　　　　　　　　　　.40　.25　.55

2 15c light green *"a"*   .55   .30   .75
3 60c dark blue *"a"*   1.00   .45   1.50

1928

Watermarked
circles.   Perforated 12.

"b"   *"c"*

4 40c reddish orange *"b"*   .35   .25   .50
5 75c bluish green *"c"*   .65   .50   .85

NEWFOUNDLAND.

The air stamps of Newfoundland are unique in that they were usually issued for some one particular flight generally of considerable historic interest. The first stamp was issued in 1919 for the attempted Atlantic crossing of Hawker and Grieve (See p. 72). The second stamp came out a month later as there were several other aspirants for the £10,000 prize still open after Hawker's failure to cross. Alcock and Brown (See p. 73) carried covers franked with these stamps and as their flight was a success, there were no further attempts that year.

In 1921 a stamp was issued for an attempted aerial route between Bostwood, Newfoundland and Halifox, Nova Scotia. Unfortunately the plane was wrecked and the stamps were disposed of to collectors.

The last stamp was issued in May, 1927, for the

Atlantic crossing of de Pinedo (See p. 77). The 1897, 60c black was surcharged "Air Mail — De Pinedo — 1927."

1919

Regular Newfoundland
   Issue of 1918
   Overprnited.

No watermark.

"*a*"

Perforated 14.

1 3c reddish brown "*a*"   (200)   850.00 650.00 750.00

1919

Regular Newfoundland
   Issue of 1897

   Overprinted.

"*b*"

Perforated 12.

2 $1 on 15c bright scarlet "*b*" (6,800) 12.00 12.00 20.00
  2a. Without comma after Post.   (2,800)   —   —   —
  2b. Without comma after Post or period
     after 1919.   (400)   —   —   —

1921 (Nov. 3)

Regular Newfoundland
   Issue of 1897
   Overprinted.
No watermark.

"*c*"

Perforated 12.

3 35c red "*c*"   (14,000) 4.00 4.00 6.00
  3a. With period after 1921.   (16,100) 5.00 5.00 7.00
  3b. Inverted surcharge.   (50) 85.00 —   —

1927

| Regular Newfoundland Issue of 1897 Overprinted. No watermark. | **Air Mail** **DE PINEDO** **1927** *"d"* | Perforated 12. |

4 60c black (De Pinedo) *"d"*   500.00 250.00 250.00

NORWAY.

A special set of Air Mail stamps was issued in 1925 to assist in the financing of the Amundsen-Ellsworth Trans-Polar Expedition flight across the North Pole. These stamps are popularly known as the "Polar" stamps and were used on the small souvenir post cards sold to help finance the Expedition. Nearly 300 pounds of these cards were carried at least a part of the way on the flight. (See p. 75).

1925

Post Horn Watermark.

Perforated 13, 14+

"a"

1	2o brownish yellow *"a"*		.08	.10	.15
2	3o bright orange *"a"*		.10	.12	.15
3	5o reddish purple *"a"*		.12	.15	.20
4	10o light green *"a"*		.15	.18	.20
5	15o deep blue *"a"*		.20	.25	.30
6	20o deep purple *"a"*		.30	.35	.40
7	25o scarlet red *"a"*		.35	.40	.50

1927 (June 13)   Perforated 13, 14+

Post Horn Watermark.

"*b*"

8 45o metallic blue "*b*"   .25   .30   .40

PERSIA.

Plans were made in 1923 to run an airline, Teheran
—Pahlevi, and stamps were printed by Messrs. Enschede
of Haarlem. This line, however, did not materialize until Feb. 12th, 1927, when the stamps previously prepared
were put on sale.

1927 (Feb.12)   Perforated 11+

Regular Persian
Issue of 1909

Overprinted.

No watermark.

"*a*"

1	1c dull red & orange	(65,000)	.10	.10	.15
2	2c dull red & violet	(30,000)	.25	.25	.30
3	3c dull red & green	(45,000)	.60	.60	.70
4	6c red & dull red	(40,000)	.20	.20	.25
5	9c dull red & gray	(35,000)	.25	.25	.30
6	10c dull red & reddish violet	(55,000)	.18	.18	.20
7	13c dull red & deep blue	(18,000)	1.20	1.20	1.40
8	26c dull red & deep green	(18,000)	1.20	1.20	1.40
9	1k dark brown, violet & silver	(20,000)	.45	.45	.55

10 2k dark brown, dark
        green & silver   (15,000)   1.65   1.65   1.75
11 3k dark brown, gray &
        silver   (11,000)   2.00   3.00   3.50
12 4k dark brown, blue &
        silver   (5,000)   4.00   8.00   9.00
13 5k dark brown, br. & gold (5,000) 4.00   8.00   9.00
14 10k dark brown, orange &
        gold   (600)   20.00 25.00 30.00
15 20k dark brown, olive green
        & gold   (600)   30.00 35.00 40.00
16 30k carmine, dark brown &
        gold   (600)   40.00 45.00 50.00

1928

Black Overprint on   Perforated 11.
Persian fiscal Stamps.

No watermark.

"*b*"   "*c*"   "*d*"

"*e*"   "*f*"

17 3k brownish yellow "*b*"   (6,000)   1.20   1.00   1.50
18 5k brown "*c*"   (6,000)   2,00   1.75   2.25

19	1t	grayish violet "d"	(6,000)	4.00	3.50	4.50
20	2t	light brown "e"	(6,000)	8.00	6.00	9.00
21	3t	dark green "f"	(6,000)	12.00	10.00	13.50

PERU.

Airmail service started between Lima and Iguitos, December 29th, 1927, using regular stamps of 1924 surcharged. The fee is 50c. for every half ounce or fraction thereof in addition to the regular fee of 2c an ounce. The use of this line saves seventeen days over the land route.

1927 (Dec. 10)
Peru Regular Issue
of 1924
Overprinted.
No watermark.

**Servicio
Aéreo**

"a"

Perforated 12.

1	50c	deep violet "a"	(5,000)	10.00	5.00	7.50

1928

"b"

2	50c	green "b"	1.50	1.25	1.75

PHILIPPINES.

On May 13th, 1926, to commemorate the successful flight from Madrid-Manila of the Spanish aviators, Captains Gallatza and Loriga the post office issued a special set of stamps from two centavos to 10 pesos. These stamps were completely sold out the morning they were issued, and as the cliches had been destroyed, new ones had to be made, and the second printing of stamps was placed on sale the following day. The two printings are almost identical.

The only flown covers with these stamps are dated May 13th, 1926, and were taken by Gallatza from Aparu to Manila.

1926
Regular Philippine Issue
of 1925 Overprinted
in red or violet.

No watermark.

Perforated 10, 11.

"a"

1	2c green *"a"*	(10,000)	2.00	2.00	3.00
2	4c rose carmine *"a"*	(9,000)	3.00	3.00	4.00
	2a. Inverted overprint.		—	—	—
3	6c lilac *"a"*	(5,000)	5.00	5.00	6.00
	3a. 6c light lilac		—	—	—
4	8c brownish orange *"a"*	(5,000)	5.00	5.00	6.00
5	10c dark blue *"a"*	(5,000)	5.00	5.00	6.00
6	12c reddish orange *"a"*	(4,000)	6.00	6.00	7.00
7	16c greenish olive (Sampson) *"a"*		—	—	—
8	16c greenish olive (Dewey) *"a"*	(4,000)	6.00	6.00	7.00
9	20c orange yellow *"a"*	(4,000)	6.00	6.00	7.00
10	26c bluish green *"a"*	(4,000)	6.00	6.00	7.00
11	30c gray *"a"*	(4,000)	6.00	6.00	7.00
12	1p lilac *"a"*	(2,000)	12.00	12.00	15.00
13	2p brown violet *"a"*	(900)	35.00	35.00	45.00
14	4p deep blue *"a"*	(700)	45.00	45.00	55.00
15	10p dark green *"a"*	(500)	55.00	55.00	65.00

POLAND.

1925 (Nov. 11)

No watermark.

Perforated 13.

"a"

1	1g pale blue *"a"*	.03	.03	.04
2	2g orange *"a"*	.03	.03	.04
3	3g brownish yellow *"a"*	.03	.03	.04
4	5g deep brown *"a"*	.05	.05	.06
5	10g green *"a"*	.06	.06	.07
6	15g reddish violet *"a"*	.08	.08	.10
7	20g greenish olive *"a"*	.12	.12	.15
8	30g rose *"a"*	.15	.15	.18
9	45g deep violet *"a"*	.20	.20	.25

ROUMANIA.

1928

Wavy Lines.
Watermarked

Perforated 11, 13+.

1	1l red brown	(20,000)	.10	.15	.20
2	2l bright blue	(20,000)	.20	.25	.30
3	5l rose	(20,000)	.50	.60	.80

RUSSIA.

The first stamp that can be attributed to Russia was
issued in a very unusual way. In the middle of July
1922, the Soviet Diplomatic representative in Berlin
ordered a series of consular stamps to be surcharged for
use on the official mail going by the air route via
Koenigsberg and Smolensk to Moscow. These stamps
were of course, not sold to the public, and as soon as
the Central Administrator at Moscow heard of this un-
authorized issue of stamps, they were ordered to be withdrawn and sent to the capitol.

Prior to November 1922, all airmail letters had been
using ordinary stamps, although there existed a considerable number of lines. At this date the 45 ruble jubilee
stamp with color changed from blue and black to green
and black was surcharged for the air mails.

The following year, fall of 1923, a series of four
stamps was printed with values in paper rubles. However, the lateness of the season prevented their use, and
by spring the currency had been changed to a gold
standard necessitating a surcharge of the issue. These
stamps therefore, were never legitimately used.

———

Imperforate.

1922 (Uov. 8)
Russian Stamps of 1922
   Overprinted with
   aeroplane in red.

No watermark.

"a"

1 45r black & green *"a"*   (100,000)   2.00   4.00   8.00

1923

Imperforate

"*b*"

2	1r reddish brown "*b*"	1.50
3	3r dark blue "*b*"	1.50
4	5r green "*b*"	2.00
5	10r carmine "*b*"	2.50

1924

Russian Stamps of 1923
  Overprinted.

No watermark.

"*c*"

6	5k on 3r dark blue "*c*"	(450,000)	.10	.10	.15
7	10k on 5r green "*c*"	(450,000)	.20	.20	.30
8	15k on 1r redish brown "*c*"	(950,000)	.30	.30	.40
8a.	Invert overprint.	(100)	—	—	—
9	20k on 10r carmine "*c*"	(1,450,000)	.30	.30	.60

1927 (Sept. 1)
  Chalky Paper.

No watermark.

Perforated 12, 13.

"*d*"

10	10k brown & ultramarine "*d*"	.20	.20	.25
11	15k greenish olive & red "*d*"	.20	.20	.25

SAAR.

"*a*"

1	50c brick red "*a*"	.06	.07	.08
2	1f deep violet "*a*"	.12	.15	.18

SIAM.

Siam was one of the first eastern countries to institute regular aerial lines. An attempted flight in February 1919 by military planes led to the installation of a regular line in March 1920 between Bangkok and Chandhaburi a distance of about 200 miles. By 1923 even the northern provinces had been connected by aerial lines.

January 3rd, 1925 marked the issuing of the first airmail stamps which were used on all the lines already ⌐. Previously ordinary stamps had been employed with special cachets, which were retained for the air stamps.

1925   Perforated 14+

No watermark.

"*a*"

1	2s yellow brown "*a*"	.25	.10	.30
2	3s brown "*a*"	.25	.10	.30
3	5s green "*a*"	.60	.20	.30

4 10s orange & black "*a*"	.70	.25	.85
5 15s carmine "*a*"	1.20	.35	1.50
6 25s deep blue "*a*"	1.50	.40	1.75
7 50s black & orange brown "*a*"	2.50	.70	3.00
8 1d brown & blue "*a*"	5.00	1.50	6.00

SPAIN.

1920 (April 4)

Regular Spanish Issue
of 1909-17 Overprinted
in red or black.

Watermarked Castle.

Perforated 13, 14.

"*a*"

1 5c green (red) "*a*"	(30,000)	.10	.15	.20
1a. Imperforated.	(200)	10.00	—	—
1b. Double overprint.		—	—	—
2 10c carmine (black) "*a*"	(30,000)	.20	.25	.30
2a. Imperforated.	(100)	20.00	—	—
3 25c dark blue (red) "*a*"	(30,000)	.35	.40	.50
3a. Inverted overprint.	(100)	20.00	—	—
3b. Double overprint.	(100)	20.00	—	—
3c. Overprint on front & back.	(200)	10.00	—	—
4 30c green "*a*"	(200)	20.00	—	—
5 50c dull blue (red) "*a*"	(30,000)	.60	.70	.85
5a. Imperforated.	(300)	8.00	—	—
6 1p lake (black) "*a*"	(30,000)	1.20	1.40	1.75
6a. Imperforated.	(100)	20.00	—	—

1926 (Sept. 15)

Gallarza Flight Issue

No watermark.

Perforated 12, 13+

"*b*"

7 15c orange & ultramarine "*b*"	(221,000)	.10	.20	.30
8 20c light green & carmine "*b*"	(238,300)	.20	.30	.40

9 30c utramarine & brown "b" (222,400) .30 .50 .60
10 40c orange brown & deep
   green "b" (225,600) .40 .75 .85
11 4p reddish purple and
   yellow "b" (31,580) 2.00 3.00 3.50

1926 (Sept. 15)
Semi-postal Air stamps

No watermark.

Perforated 12, 13.

"c"

12 5c violet & black "c" (200,500) .10 .15 .20
13 10c black & ultramarine "c" (216,000) .20 .30 .35
14 25c black & carmine "c" (220,180) .30 .40 .50
15 50c black & reddish
   orange "c" (221,300) .50 .60 .70
16 1p green & black "c" (111,000) .60 .75 .85

1927

Gallarza Flight Issue.
Overprinted.   Perforated 12, 13.

No watermark.

17 15c orange & ultramarine
   (brown) "b" (79,000) .15 .20 .35
18 20c green & carmine (blue) "b" (81,700) .25 .35 .50
19 30c deep brown & ultramarine
   (red) "a" (77,600) .35 .50 .70
20 40c brown orange & green
   (brown) "b" (74,400) .50 .75 1.00
21 4p yellow & reddish purple
   (blue) "b" (18,420) 2.50 3.00 3.75

1927

Semi-postal Air Stamps   Perforated **12, 13.**
   of 1926
   Overprinted.

   No watermark.

22	5c violet & black (red) "*c*" (99,500)	.15	.20	.30
23	10c black & ultramarine (red) "*b*" (70,000)	.30	.35	.50
24	25c black & carmine (blue) "*c*" (70,000)	.40	.50	.75
25	50c black & reddish orange (blue) "*c*" (70,000)	.75	1.00	1.25
26	1p green & black (red) "*c*" (39,000)	1.00	1.50	2.00

Same with Additional
   Overprint of new   Perforated **12, 13.**
    values.

   No watermark.

27	75c on 5c violet & black "*c*" (50,000)	.50	.60	.75
28	75c on 10c black & ultramarine "*c*" (14,000)	1.00	1.25	1.50
29	75c on 25c black & carmine "*c*" (9,820)	1.50	170	2.25
30	75c on 50c black & reddish orange "*c*" (8,700)	1.75	2.25	3.00

SWEDEN.

Air stamps were issued on September 17th, 1920 for the regular lines, Malmo—Warnemunde and Copenhagen—Stockholm, by surcharging official stamps of 1910-1919. They were withdrawn in January 1922, and regular stamps used in their place.

The inverted surcharges have been conterfeited.

1920 (Sept. 17)
Swedish Official Stamps
of 1918-18 Overprinted
in dark blue.

Watermarked Wavy
Lines

Perforated 13+.

"*a*"

1 10ö on 3ö dull brown "*a*"		.30	.20	.50
1a. Inverted overprint.	(100)	35.00	—	—
2 20ö on 2ö light orange "*a*"		.50	.40	.75
2a. Inverted overprint.	(300)	15.00	—	—
3 50ö on 4ö violet "*a*"		1.25	1.00	2.00
3a. Inverted overprint.	(300)	15.00	—	—

Watermarked Crown.   Perforated 13.

4 20ö on 2ö light orange "*a*"	(500)	150.00	150.00	250.00
5 50ö on 4ö violet "*a*"	(1,000)	15.00	12.00	18.00

SWITZERLAND.

By 1913 aviation had gotten a solid foothold in
Switzerland and approximately fifteen independent mail
flights took place that year. A dozen different semi
official and private stamps were issued as well as various
cards and labels.

The government, took no hand in any of the flights
until the spring of 1919 when regular routes were opened and run throughout the summer. In October operations ceased, and the government withdrew its interest
on account of the expense involved. The lines were
leased to private concerns the following year.

It is claimed by certain Swiss Philatelists that their's
was the first country to issue any type of air stamp,
though of course of an unofficial nature.

1919-20 (April 30)
Regular Issue of
Switzerland 1907-08
Overprinted in carmine.

Watermarked
Greek Cross.

Perforated 11+.

"*a*"

1 50c light green & dark
    green "*a*"   (500,000) 1.50 1.75 2.00

1920 (Nov. 11)

2 30c light green & yellow
    brown "*a*"   (100,000) 4.50 6.50 9.00

1923 (March 1)

Watermarked
Greek Cross.

Perforated 11, 12   & comp.

"*b*"

"*c*"   "*d*"

3 15c pale green & brownish
    red "*b*"   (140,000) .10 .12 .15
4 20c pale green & green "*b*"   .15 .20 .25
5 25c blue & deep blue "*b*"   (140,000) .15 .18 .25
6 35c light brown & brown "*b*" (140,000) .20 .25 .35
7 40c violet "*c*"   (140,000) .25 .30 .40

8 45c dark blue & red *"c"*   (140,000)   .30   .35   .50
9 50c black & red *"d"*   (140,000)   .40   .45   .65

1924 (May 13)   Perforated 11+.

"e"

10 65c dark blue & grayish blue *"e"*   .40   .50   .60
11 75c red brown & orange *"e"*   .50   .60   .75
12   1 fr violet & dark violet *"e"*   .60   .70   .90

SYRIA.

Aerial lines in Syria as in the other French posses-
sions have been entirely military. They carry both
mail and passengers on regular schedule as in commercial lines, and so serve a double purpose.

Operations started in December 1920 when lines
were opened between Aleppo — Alexandritta and Aleppo — Deir el Zoor, Damascus —Swedia, and Damascus
— Palymra, and between Latakia and Homs which was
later supplemented by a line from Alaouites.

1920 (Dec. 1)

Regular French Issue of 1920	These Designs
Overprinted.	Overprinted.
No watermark.	Perforated 12, 13+

"a"   *"b"*

1   1pi on 5c green *"a"*   (5,000) 10.00 4.00 5.00
    1a. Double overprint.   35.00
2   5pi on 15c light green *"a"*   (3,500) 12.00 6.00 7.00
3   10pi on 40c red & blue *"b"*   (3,500) 12.00 6.00 7.00

1921 (June 12)

Same overprint on French Issue of 1921.
No watermark.

4   1pi on 20c reddish brown
        "a"   (2,000) 15.00 7.00   8.00
5   5pi on 1fr greenish olive
        & claret *"a"*   (1,000) 25.00 10.00 12.00
6   10pi on 2fr light blue &
        orange *"b"*   (1,000) 25.00 10.00 12.00

1921 (Oct. 6)

Regular French Issue of 1921
Overprinted vertically.

No watermark.

"c"

7   1pi on 20c reddish brown *"c"* (11,000) 2.00 1.50 3.00
8   5pi on 1fr greenish olive &
        claret *"c"*   (5'500) 6.50 2.00 4.00
9   10pi on 2fr light blue &
        orange *"c"*   (5,500) 6.50 2.00 4.00
    9a. Double overprint.   20.00   —   —

1922 (May 29)

Regular French Issue of 1921
Overprinted.

No watermark.

"d"

10   2pi on 40c light blue &
        red *"d"*   (10,000) 1.50 1.00 2.00

11	3pi on 60c ultramarine & violet "d"	(10,000)	1.50	1.00	2.00
12	5pi on 1fr greenish olive & claret "d"	(10,000)	1.50	1.00	2.00
13	10pi on 2fr light blue & orange "d"	(10,000)	1.50	1.00	2.00

1923 (Nov. 22)

 Regular French Issue of 1923
 Overprinted as before.

 No watermark.

"e"

14	2pi on 40c light blue & red "e"	(3,000)	5.00	4.00	6.00
15	3pi on 60c ultramarine & violet "e"	(3,000)	5.00	4.00	6.00
16	5pi on 1fr greenish olive & claret "e"	(3,000)	5.00	4.00	6.00
17	10pi on 2fr light blue and orange "e"	(3,000)	5.00	4.00	6.00
	17a Double overprint.		—	—	—

1924 (Jan. 13)

 Regular French Issue of 1924

 Overprinted as before.

"f"

18	2pi on 40c light blue & red "f"	(15,750)	.75	.65	.95
19	3pi on 60 ultramarine & violet "f"	(15,750)	.75	.60	.95
	19a. Inverted overprint.		—	—	—
20	5pi on 1fr greenish olive & claret "f"	(15,750)	.75	.60	.95
21	10pi on 2fr light blue & orange "f"	(15,750)	.75	.60	.95

1924 (July 17)

Regular French Issue of 1924
Overprinted.

"*g*"

22	2pi on 40c light blue & red "*g*"	(45,000)	.40	.35	.60
23	3pi on 60c ultramarine & violet "*g*"	(45,300)	.40	.35	.60
24	5pi on 1fr greenish olive & claret "*g*"	(51,000)	.40	.35	.60
25	10pi on 2fr light blue & orange "*g*"	(48,250)	.40	.35	.60

1925

Regular Syria Issue
of 1925
Overprinted in green.

A V I O N

طيارة

"*h*"

26	2pi deep brown "*h*"	.15	.15	.30
27	3pi brownish orange "*h*"	.20	.20	.40
28	5pi violet "*h*"	.30	.30	.50
29	10pi brownish violet "*h*"	.60	.60	.85

1926

Regular Syria Issue
of 1925
Overprinted
aeroplane in red.

"*i*"

30	2pi deep brown "*i*"	.10	.10	.20
31	3pi brownish orange "*i*"	.15	.15	.30
32	5pi violet "*i*"	.25	.25	.40
33	10pi brownish violet "*i*"	.50	.50	.85

TUNIS.

A stamp was issued on April 20th, 1919 for the lines from Tunis to Gabes, Zarzis and Ben-Gardane. Service ceased on February 20th, 1920 and the stamp was re-called. In the meantime, a second stamp had been printed for this line, which however was not ready until two months after the aerial line closed. This stamp is therefore not known "Flown" except on the Tunis — Paris flight of July 6th, 1922.

1919 (April 20)

Regular Issues Overprinted.   Perforated 13, 14.
    No watermark.

"*a*"

1 30c on 35c brown & greenish
      olive "*a*"   (75,000)   .60 1.20 2.00
    1a. Inverted overprint.   —   —   —
    1b. Double overprint.   —   —   —
    1c. Double overprint, inverted. —   —   —
2 30c blue, rose & greenish olive (100,000)   .50 .60 .85

1924 (March 24)
    Overprinted.

"*b*"   "*c*"

3   1fr dark blue & ultramarine
    "*b*"   (300,000)   .35.   .45   .60

4   2fr pink, red & green "*b*" (100,000) 1.00 1.25 1.50
5 1.75fr on 75c red & vermilion
       "*b*"   (300,000) .35 .45 .60
6 1.75fr on 5fr green & violet "*c*" (75,000) 1.50 2.00 3.00

1928 (Feb. 21)

Blue Overprint.

Perforated 13+, **14.**

"*d*"

7 1.30fr pale violet & orange "*d*"   .20 .20 .40
8 1.80fr red & green "*d*"   .30 .30 .50
9 2.55fr brown & lilac "*d*"   .40 .40 .60

UNION OF SOUTH AFRICA.

1925 (March 2)

Unwatermarked.

Perforated **12.**

"*a*"

1 1p dull red "*a*"   (65,390) .40 .80 1.00
2 3p ultramarine """   (75,621) .35 .70 1.00
3 6p violet "*a*"   (53,536) .55 1.25 1.**75**
4 9p light green "*a*"   (27,763) 1.50 3.00 4.00

URUGUAY.

A Montevideo — Rocha line was opened March 22nd, 1921 and the first stamp issued. About 300 letters and cards were carried to Rocha, and a very small number on the return trip to Montevideo. Counterfeits of the black surcharge (la) are known, and hard to distinguish, as they are made by chemically treating the ordinary blue surcharge.

The second stamp was issued on the occasion of a town fair at Mercedes, November 12th, 1921 when a flight took place between there and Montevideo, 500 covers were carried.

The third issue in October 1923, came out to commemorate the battle of Sarandi Grande and a flight took place between there and the capitol, carrying 880 covers.

The 1924 issue came out January 2nd for service Montevideo — Buenos Ayres. It is not very well printed and shows many minor varities not worth listing.

The little stork stamps were used only on August 25th, 1925, the centenary of the Assembly of Florida, (Uruguay), on letters carried by airplane between Montevideo and Florida or vice versa. The stamps were not delivered to the public but were affixed to the letters and cancelled at the post office. Later uncancelled copies appeared on the market.

The 45c blue was used only on September 24th, 1925, the centenary of the battle of Rincon. Like the preceding stamps this was affixed and cancelled in the post office.

1921 (Nov. 12)

Stamps of Uruguay
Overprinted in dark
blue, red or green.

No watermark.

"a"

Perforated. 11+.

1 25c dark brown (blue) *"a"* (10,000)   7.00   7.00   9.00
  1a.   Black overprint.   (100)   30.00   —   —
2 25c dark brown (red) *"a"* (15,000)   3.00   3.00   5.00
  2a.   Inverted overprint.   (100)   30.00   —   —
3 25c dark brown (green) *"a"* (15,000)   3.00   3.00   5.00

1924 (Jan. 3)  Perforated 11+.

Watermarked

"b"

4   6c deep blue *"b"*   (50,000)   .80   1.00   1.25
  4a.   No period after R.   (2,000)   3.50   5.00   6.50
5 10c scarlet red *"b"*   (30,000)   1.20   2.00   2.50
6 20c dark green *"b"*   (20,000)   1.80   2.50   3.00

1925 (Aug. 25)  Perforated 12+.

Inscribed, "Montevideo"

Watermarked.

"c"

7 14c black & blue *"c"*   (7,100)   12.50   8.00   10.00
      Inscribed "Florida"
8 14c black & blue *"c"*   (7,100)   12.50   8.00   10.00

1925 (Sept. 25)   Perforated 11.

"d"

9 45c bluish green *"d"*   (15,328)   —   3.50   5.00

1926

Imperforated.

Watermarked.

"e"

10	6c	deep blue "e"	(50,000)	.50	.60	.75
11	10c	vermilion "e"	(30,000)	.80	1.00	1.25
12	20c	bluish green "e"	(20,000)	1.50	2.00	2.50
13	25c	violet "e"	(20,000)	1.50	2.00	2.50

1928

14	10c	light green "e"	(30,000)	.40	.30	—
15	20c	orange "e"	(30,000)	.70	.60	—
16	30c	dark blue "e"	(20,000)	.90	80	—
17	38c	green "e"	(30,000)	.90	.60	—
18	40c	yellow "e"	(20,000)	1.00	.80	—
19	50c	violet "e"	(10,000)	4.50	4.00	—
20	76c	orange "e"	(30,000)	2.50	2.00	—
21	1p	reddish lake "e"	(10,000)	4.50	4.00	—
22	1.14p	dark blue "e"	(20,000)	4.00	3.50	—
23	1.52p	yellow "e"	(20,000)	4.00	3.50	—
24	1.90p	violet "e"	(10,000)	4.50	4.00	—
25	3.80p	reddish lake "e"	(10,000)	7.00	6.00	—

The Graf Zeppelin 1928

The recent history making flights of this graceful monarch of the skies from her home port to America and return were followed with intense interest by all. Many thousands of us were thrilled by the splendid picture she presented sailing above our great cities.

The following covers carried on this epoch making flight are available:

1. Westward flight, Germany to U. S.   Card $3.00 net.
2. Westward flight, Germany to U. S. Cover $7.00 net.
3. Eastward flight, U. S. to Germany   Cover $3.00 net

K. Lissiuk Philatelic Co., Inc.

1476 BROADWAY

New York, N. Y.

The Amundsen Postcard

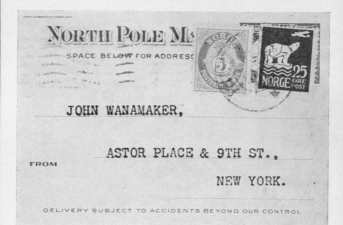

A striking souvenier of his intrepid dash toward the Pole by Aeroplane in 1924.

"Amundsen's exploits in the frozen north will never be forgotten nor will anyone attempt to depreciate the solemnity of his death. This is a noble cavalier who in search of Nobile flew forth into the land of ice, never to return."

Souvenir card of 1919 attempt — $1.50 net.

K. Lissiuk Philatelic Co., Inc.

1476 BROADWAY

New York, N. Y.

INDEX

===

INDEX (*Continued*)